Don   Delano   11.95

D1095680

MYTH

CONTENTS

MYTH

MOIRA KERR
JOHN BENNETT

Copp Clark Pitman Ltd.
Toronto

Moira C. Kerr, B.A. (Hist.)

John A. E. Bennett, B.A. (Eng.),
M.Ed., O.S.A.

© Copyright 1966

Copp Clark Publishing

ISBN 0-7730-2305-4

Printed and bound in Canada.

Copp Clark Pitman Ltd.
495 Wellington Street West
Toronto, Ontario   M5V 1E9

FOREWORD

Myth was written in the belief that mythology can be both a fascinating subject in itself and the gateway to a deeper understanding of art, literature and history.

Myths and legends did not simply spring into being; they were attempts by ancient peoples to understand and communicate something deeply meaningful in their lives. Looked at in this light, myths cease to appear fanciful fairy-tales and become stories from the deepest heart of mankind.

Artists and writers who have sensed the importance of myths have woven them into the whole fabric of our culture. Any attempt to understand the greater part of our cultural heritage necessarily involves a knowledge of the tales of mythology.

Myth does not pretend to be a comprehensive anthology of myth and legend. To gather together all the tales of Greek mythology alone, with their variety of versions, would require many volumes. Instead, this book presents a few of the better-known myths which are of considerable importance to our culture.

The myths and legends contained in this volume have been told in their simplest form, with many names and details omitted, in the belief that the simplest story is the most direct route to understanding.

Copious notes have been included in this volume. We hope that they will be used for enrichment only, and that only the narratives will be required material for study.

Some of the stories have been related to literary works built around them. In these cases, the emphasis has been entirely upon the way the myth has been used. No attempt has been made to trace the mythological allusions which abound in our literature, for knowledge of the myths themselves make such allusions quite clear. Fairly extensive notes are provided on the epic poets Homer and Virgil, and the tragedians Aeschylus, Sophocles, and Euripides.

Secondly, in some instances the stories have been related to the historical background. Such references are not intended to be dogmatic, for the number of historical theories about some myths defies count. They are merely suggestions which have been made about the origin or meaning of a certain myth, and are intended merely to arouse interest in the myth itself by giving to it a possible place and time.

Other notes consider the use of certain myths in art, particularly in painting of the Renaissance and later periods, and in words and phrases which have become a part of our language.

In all notes, the works selected or the events chosen are not intended to be comprehensive, or to represent our view of the best uses of the myth. Our intention has been merely to open windows through which the reader may see some of the fields illuminated by mythology.

M. C. K.

J. A. E. B.

INTRODUCTION

THE ILLUSTRATIONS

The Cover Design

From earliest times fabulous monsters have been represented in art by combining parts of different animals. The winged lions on the cover are ornaments between the capitals of the columns on the temple of Apollo Didymaeus near Miletus.

The design across the top of the cover is the Greek Fret, or Meander border, which is a specifically Greek ornament. The fact that it is based on a regular network suggests a textile origin. The name "meander" is said to be derived from the river in Asia Minor, the Maeandros, now the Menderes, which flows in sinuous curves. Greek vase-painting and architecture also give rise to variations of the pattern.

The Map—Homer's World

This map was drawn from a reproduction of one of the earliest maps representing the world as it was known in Homer's time.

The Decorations

Each story in *Myth* is accompanied by a symbolic design. When a particular object is represented, the design has been inspired by an authentic representation of the place and period required. Outstanding among the sources have been Greek vase-paintings and relief carvings, although these pictures have been stylized for the sake of the design. The terra cotta, white, and black have been selected to suggest original Greek pottery.

Every attempt has been made to free the imagination of the reader by avoiding representation of faces of mortals and gods.

THE FORMS

Although a variety of story types are often gathered together under the heading **mythology**, there is a clear distinction among them.

The basic type is the **myth** itself. A myth is a story by which ancient people attempted to account for things which they experienced. Primitive man was faced by a world full of wonder, and asked himself the questions which children of today still ask: Where did the world come from? Who made men and women? Why does it get dark at night? What happens to the sun when it sets? Why do crops grow in summer and not in winter? He had no one to answer those questions, so he tried to explain things to himself in terms of the things he actually knew.

If the sun moved across the sky, primitive man reasoned, something must be pulling it, just as earthly horses pull a chariot. If the crops stopped growing during a certain season, some great being must be forbidding the earth to produce them. Thus the stories that primitive men told involved beings greater than men— supernatural beings, who looked and acted like men, but escaped all the limitations that bound ordinary beings.

Not only did myths try to explain natural phenomena, they also evolved explanations for rituals and ceremonies which were passed down from generation to generation. Every primitive group had certain rituals sacred to them alone, varying from the most casual to what would seem to us grotesque and horrible. Often, as the actual reason for performing such rituals faded over the years, people invented a new explanation, usually making the origin more dignified and acceptable than it really had been.

Many of the gods who peopled the myths developed from early animistic deities. Very early man believed that the things around him had spirits within them which were to be worshipped. They inhabited trees, streams, even stones. Some such spirits were given such respect that their worship lasted even after men had passed from animism; they were translated into more powerful deities.

Early myths were probably very simple, but they changed with countless retellings and re-enactments. Some became tremendously complicated, being told in several versions; they became confused with other myths, so that the same basic story acquired two sets of characters; sometimes they were deliberately developed to correspond with the religious beliefs of a certain group. As we have them today, the myths of Greece alone would require several volumes to relate.

A second form, one often confused with the pure myth, is the **legend**. In most cases, the legend deals with the same supernatural figures as do the myths; however, pure myth is a creation of the imagination, while legend has a germ of actual historical truth in it. The central character in a legend is usually a hero, a mortal man who performs wonderful deeds. Legends originated in the deeds of men, but through frequent retelling the deeds assumed an impossible or almost-impossible dimension, and the heroes themselves took on some of the character-istics of supernatural beings. The stories of Heracles and Jason are clear examples of legend.

Another form which is closely linked to myth in content, but not in purpose, is the classical **epic**. An epic is a long narrative, usually composed by one poet, and usually having considerable scope in time, space, and characters; it too has a hero of noble, sometimes even godly, origin who performs great deeds of valour. However, an epic is national in character, and intends to arouse in its readers or listeners a great pride in their country.

The stories told in the three great classical epics—the Greek *Iliad* and *Odyssey* and the Roman *Aeneid*—are included in a collection of myths because they number the gods and goddesses of mythology among their characters, and because they present the best form of many myths and legends.

A fourth form, the classical **drama** is, like the epic, the product of an original creative genius, writing for an audience. Greek drama was closely linked to mythology, however, in two ways. First, drama originated in orgiastic rituals carried on in honour of Dionysus, the god of wine. Frenzied rites gradually assumed a form from which developed, slowly, the literary form we know as drama.

Secondly, many of the greatest of the Greek dramas were dramatizations of the stories of mythology, with, of course, interpretations inserted by the dramatist. Of the thirty or so plays which have survived from the amazing volume of works written by the three masters of tragedy, Aeschylus, Sophocles, and Euripides, only one, Aeschylus' *Persians*, is based on other than mythological or legendary material.

Because the four forms often deal with the same or similar characters and recount similar episodes, it is easy to forget that they are all very different from one another. Pure myth tries to explain, and is related to religion and philosophy. Pure legend is a form which aims primarily at entertainment. Epic is intended to stimulate patriotism, and classical drama, the most personal of the forms, is one author's attempt to find understanding of the human situation.

OUR SOURCES FOR THE MYTHS

It is not difficult for us to picture the circumstances in which the early myths were passed on from one generation to another. They were told in village market places and around the watch-fires, at gatherings of the whole tribe, around the family fire to children and adults alike. Whenever people sought answers, or wished the entertainment of a good story, myths and legends were popular.

Sometimes a wandering bard, or minstrel, would visit the village or the court of a great noble. He was always welcomed warmly, for he could hold his audience spellbound while he spun a tale, new and exciting or old and familiar, of gods and heroes.

The stories sometimes changed from telling to telling, for they were recorded only in the memory of the poet. As a story became more familiar and beloved by a group, and so became a part of the cultural heritage they wished to pass on to their children and grandchildren, many young people would be given the task of committing a whole poem—perhaps thousands of lines—to memory.

In later times the poems were finally written down, and they still belong to us after almost three thousand years.

The most famous early works preserved in this way were the *Iliad* and the *Odyssey*, which we attribute to Homer.

Other early works which pass on to us many of the stories of mythology are the thirty-four works known as *Homeric hymns*. These were composed not by Homer but by later bards, living during a period which stretched over several centuries until perhaps 450 B.C. Before presenting a recitation at one of the large public festivals, the bard would usually deliver a prologue in the form of a hymn to honour the god to whom the festival was dedicated. Many of these hymns contained elaborate references to popular myths about the gods concerned.

One other early Greek poet who included many myths in his compositions was Hesiod, a shepherd and farmer who lived in the eighth and ninth century B.C. One of his works is a poem called *Theogony*, a full account of the creation of the world and an outline of many of our stories of the gods.

The fifth century B.C. was the golden age of Greece, when some of the greatest writers of all time were living. Among those important to mythology were Pindar, a poet whose odes in celebration of the victors at national games embodied many myths, and the three great tragedians, Aeschylus, Sophocles, and Euripides. Almost all their plays are concerned with myths. Another important source was the comic playwright Aristophanes.

Many later Greek writers, including not only poets but the historian Herodotus and the philosopher Plato, devoted some part of their writings to discussion or retelling of myths.

Some of the greatest sources, however, are Roman writers. The Romans greatly admired Greek culture, and freely imitated its achievements in almost all the arts. Their study of Greek poetry taught them many myths, and, of course, many myths and legends were incorporated in their own religious belief. Two Romans are outstanding: Virgil, who wrote Rome's national epic, the *Aeneid*, and Ovid.

Ovid may well be called the greatest myth-collector of all. His major work is a book called *Metamorphoses*, in which he tells dozens of our most familiar stories with a grace and style which have delighted readers for two thousand years.

A glance at the list of writers who have handed down a few of the more famous myths will indicate the variety of sources we acknowledge. The stories of the Trojan war are drawn chiefly from Homer and Virgil; Jason, from Pindar; Medea, from Euripides; Daedalus, from a writer named Apollodorus; Psyche, from a Roman writer, Apuleius; Demeter, from a Homeric hymn; Narcissus, Pygmalion, Phaëthon, and many others, from Ovid.

SYMBOLISM

A study of mythology on any but the surface level necessarily involves a study of symbolism, the use of concrete things to represent other, usually abstract, things.

There are two basic ways in which mythology and symbolism are connected. The simpler is our turning of a mythological character, or event, or place, into a symbol, because by its constant use it has come to mean much the same thing to most people. In this way, Heracles has become a symbol of strength, Aphrodite of romantic love, the various monsters of evil, to mention but a few examples. The understanding of such symbols depends, of course, upon familiarity with the myth, or at least with enough of it to know how to identify the character or event mentioned.

This type of symbol from mythology has always been greatly used in literature, art, and common expression.

The other type of symbolism is the use of symbols within the myth. In this sense, mythology is said to be a symbolic language by which ancient peoples expressed what was to them a truth.

Some of the symbols used in mythology would have meaning only to persons who knew their origin. For example, one common symbol in certain myths is the bull; to people living at a particular time in particular parts of the world, the bull would immediately suggest the powerful island of Crete, for there the bull was held sacred and its likeness was raised over almost everything that had to do with the island.

In a broader sense, however, the bull would have a symbolic meaning to everyone, for it represents strength and, by extension, a driving, mindless force.

The present century has seen a tremendous surge of interest in this second type of mythological symbol. The new interest has sprung from the relatively new sciences of the mind, particularly from the field which may loosely be called **psychoanalysis**. Psychoanalysis deals with the study of the unconscious part of man's mind, and its leaders have unearthed what they claim to be symbols meaningful to everyone. These symbols appear in the dreams of individuals and in the myths of groups.

The most important studies of mythology and psychological symbols were conducted by Carl Gustav Jung. In addition to his training and experience as a psychologist and his founding of the school of analytical psychology, Jung was a classical scholar and had a vast knowledge of mythology. He identified certain symbols which he claimed were stored in some dim part of every person's mind, and these he named **archetypes**. This theory explains, according to Jung, why similar figures appear so often in the myths of all nations, in fairy tales, religion, and in dreams.

One of the most important archetypes seen in mythology, according to Jung, is what he calls the "archetype of meaning", which may be generally understood as wisdom or somewhat magical power. The figure representing magical power is usually the old wise man who may be a prophet, a king, a magician, hero, or saviour. The appearance of the old wise man in myth or dream is understood by Jung's followers to represent the qualities of wisdom and power that man feels in his subconscious and which, if awakened, may lead a man to believe that he is really endowed with powers beyond the reach of ordinary men.

Another important archetype who can be identified over and over in mythology is the "great mother." She represents the qualities associated with mothers: loving, protecting, helping, and understanding.

PART ONE

THE GODS

THE BEGINNING

Throughout the ages, men have attempted to explain how the world and the life upon it came into being.

Ancient Greeks, like all peoples of the early world, sought a satisfying explanation of the beginnings of things by attributing divine qualities to natural phenomena around them. Many tales were told to explain the world's origin, but three of these became more popular than the rest.

One story claimed that the source of everything was Oceanus, the spirit of the river which they believed flowed around the edges of the earth. A second tale, popular among ancient philosophers, saw life as originating from the union of Night and the rushing Wind. Their firstborn, says this story, was Eros, or Love, who later brought into being all life in the world.

A third story was told by a farmer-poet who lived in Greece about the eighth century B.C. Hesiod was the first of the Greeks to attempt a classification of the stories of gods and goddesses. The following story of the origin of the earth and its life is taken from Hesiod's *Theogony*.

8

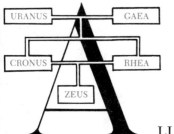

LL that existed in the beginning was Chaos, the formless, vast and black emptiness. Then appeared Gaea, the Earth, whose snowy mountains and fertile valleys were to become the dwelling places of the gods. Third was created Love, or Eros, whose heart-softening influence would be felt in the formation of beings.

Gaea became the great mother of all things. She first gave birth to Uranus, the starlit sky, as a cloak to envelop her in sleep, and with his birth the universe was created.

Then Gaea and Uranus produced the first race, the Titans. There were twelve of these giants: six male, one of whom was named Cronus, and six female, one of whom was Rhea.

The Titans were followed by other giants who resembled them, but had only one eye in the middle of their foreheads; they were called the Cyclops. Finally Gaea bore three gigantic monsters, the Hecatoncheires, or Hundred-Handed Ones, each with fifty heads and a hundred powerful arms.

When Uranus saw his offspring he recoiled in horror and shut them up in Tartarus, the innermost part of the earth, so remote that it would take an anvil falling from the surface nine days to reach it. At first Gaea mourned for her children, especially for the Titans whom she loved most dearly. Afterwards she grew angry, and planned a dark scheme of revenge against her husband.

Gaea took counsel with her sons, hidden deep within her.

"Who will help me?" she asked each in turn. Only Cronus, the last-born, was brave enough to volunteer. Arming himself with a sickle which his mother had created for him from grey iron in her body, he waited in hiding. As soon as Uranus grew dark upon the earth, Cronus leaped upon him and dealt him a terrible wound which maimed him forever.

From the drops of crimson blood which seeped into the earth sprang the Erinnyes or Furies, those relentless beings who pursue and torment the guilty. And as the mutilated parts of the body of Uranus floated on the waves of the summer sea, they broke into a white foam from which was born a young goddess, Aphrodite.

THE WAR WITH
THE TITANS

AFTER Cronus had disposed of Uranus, he released his brothers and sisters from their prison in the underworld, and they gratefully acknowledged him as leader of the Titans and ruler of the universe.

However, he too proved a proud and jealous monarch, who feared that someone else would overthrow him just as he had overthrown his father. One of his first deeds was to shut the Cyclops and the Hundred-Handed Ones back in Tartarus, lest they rebel against him. His own children he feared even more, for the earth had whispered to him a prophecy that one day a son would destroy him. Cronus was constantly vigilant, and over and over he repeated the same means of preventing such a son from challenging him. As soon as his wife Rhea gave birth to a child, the king of the Titans seized and devoured the infant.

Horrified at having her children thus torn from her, poor Rhea eventually resolved that one, at least, should live. She went to a far-off mountain, and there in a cave gave birth to a son. She entrusted the infant to the care of nymphs, and, to conceal from her husband what she had done, she wrapped a stone in swaddling-clothes and showed it to him. Cronus snatched the stone and swallowed it, thinking it to be the son who, unknown to him, was growing strong on milk and honey in the land of Crete. On the shoulders of this son, Zeus, was to fall the destiny which Cronus had dreaded.

As soon as he had grown to manhood, Zeus went to his mother Rhea and with her help secured the position of cup-bearer to his father. He soon found an opportunity to mix certain poisons in the king's honeyed drink. All unsuspecting, Cronus drained the poisoned cup and was seized with racking pain; he began to vomit, and from his throat poured first the stone which he had taken for his child, then, whole, unharmed and fully-grown, the other offspring he had swallowed.

The brothers and sisters of Zeus, freed at last from their terrible imprisonment, asked him to be their leader in a war to dethrone the tyrannous Titan.

The war between the Titans and the brothers and sisters of Zeus lasted ten years. The old giants had two leaders, for since Cronus was past his fighting prime, a younger Titan named Atlas was named the leader for battle. Zeus led the younger gods, and with his brothers Hades and Poseidon as his closest advisers, set up a fortress on the heights of cloud-ridden Mount Olympus.

The Titans, armed with huge boulders and with tall trees torn out of the forest, tried time and time again to climb Mount Olympus and dislodge the young gods, but Zeus obscured their vision with dark clouds and blinded them with lightning. Each time the Titans advanced they were cast down.

After his followers had suffered many defeats, Cronus conceived a plan.

"Let us build a mountain even higher than Olympus, and from there hurl our boulders down on the heads of the upstart gods!"

The Titans went to work tearing huge pieces out of Mount Ossa and piling them upon Mount Pelion, making one large mountain out of the two. The mass of rock soon was level with the highest peak of Mount Olympus.

Meanwhile, Zeus too had been considering strategy. He made a long journey to the underworld to release from Tartarus the old Cyclops whom Cronus had imprisoned there, and with them the Hundred-Handed Ones. In gratitude, the one-eyed monsters gave great gifts to the leaders of the Olympians. To Zeus himself they gave the thunder-bolt which ever afterwards was to be his symbol and source of power.

His brother Hades received a helmet of darkness, and Poseidon was given a trident. Armed with these weapons, the three brothers held a council of war and decided upon new plans.

Soon afterwards, Hades crept under cover of his helmet of darkness to steal the weapons of his father Cronus. At the same time, Poseidon distracted the old Titan with his trident, while Zeus manoeuvred himself into a position where he could smite him with the thunderbolt.

The stratagem meant the end of the rule of the Titans, for when Zeus gave the signal all the Olympians seized freshly-wrought thunderbolts from the hands of the Cyclops and hurled them with devastating effect. The Titans fell back, shielding their bodies from the onslaught, and the Hundred-Handed Ones took advantage of the lull to fling rocks with all hands at once. The Titans' proud new mountain shifted on its foundations, and with a roar collapsed.

Zeus and his brothers took power quickly. Their punishment of the war leader, Atlas, was intended to be an example to all who would threaten the power of Olympus, for he was forced to support the sky on his shoulders forever. The new rulers spared Rhea and the Titanesses, but banished the Titans themselves to the most westerly island on earth, to live alone there in payment for the cruel deeds of their king, Cronus.

The victorious brothers drew lots to divide the universe. Hades won the underworld, land of terror and darkness; Poseidon gained the sea. Zeus won as his realm the sky, and from the top of Mount Olympus reigned as supreme ruler of the earth and king of the gods.

ECHOES IN LITERATURE

Cronus has been a popular subject for English writers as well as classical ones. In general, he is portrayed as a dark and evil-boding figure, although the age over which he ruled is considered the happiest of all times. Some writers assigned to him the responsibility for most of the evils which still beset humanity.

One writer, John Keats, gave a quite different portrait of Cronus (under his Latin name Saturn) in his long poem Hyperion. This picture, which shows Cronus as filled with sadness because he has lost the power to help mankind, is almost the only sympathetic portrayal of him in English literature.

References to Cronus' wife Rhea in English literature usually call her by the more beautiful Cybele, her name in Phrygia and other countries of the Near East.

12

THE AGES OF MAN

THE passing of the Titans brought the death of the first and loveliest epoch of man's history.

The years when the Titans ruled were called the Golden Age, for men were carefree and innocent. No fear existed in the whole world, and all creatures were happy. Even the animals had no cause for terror, for men lived on milk and honey and the fruits of the earth.

This wonderful time was followed by the Silver Age, when men were less pure and less good, and knew fear. They no longer lived solely on the gifts of the gods, but cooked grain into bread. They also were quarrelsome, although they stopped short of making war, and they refused to acknowledge the gods. Every one of them was destroyed by Zeus.

Next came men of the Brazen Age, who ate the flesh of other creatures and, armed with weapons of bronze, made war on one another. Most were lowly and brutal creatures, but among them lived a few who had elements of godliness and became glorious in the eyes of their fellow men as heroes.

The last of mankind's ages was the Iron Age, which fostered men of cruelty, injustice, dishonesty, greed, and treachery, inevitably destined to be struck down by Zeus.

Discrepancies exist among the myths: "The Ages of Man"
told of human and animal life on earth during even the
time of Cronus; "Prometheus" tells that they were not
created until during the reign of Zeus.

PROMETHEUS

TWO of the Titans had turned from their own people to side with Zeus in the war of the gods. They were not banished like their brothers, but were given one of the most important and honoured tasks that the victorious Olympians had to offer.

To these two, the brothers Prometheus and Epimetheus, was entrusted the duty of creating living beings to inhabit the world. The younger brother, Epimetheus, set himself immediately to the task, and made an interesting variety of creatures. In typical fashion, however, (for his name meant "Afterthought"), he blithely gave away all the best gifts first. To some creatures he gave warm fur, to others, colourful feathers; some received majestic wings which enabled them to soar above the clouds, and others were given fins which allowed them to probe the depths of the ocean. To some animals Epimetheus gave great strength, to some he gave great speed, and to some, great beauty. Then, when the time came to create man, there was nothing left.

The elder brother, Prometheus (whose name meant "Forethought"), considered the plight of this poor helpless creature made in his own form, and wondered what he could do for him. No fur covered the shivering body. There was not much strength in the puny limbs. Since he walked on only two legs, man could not move very quickly. Most important of all, he did not even have any natural protection such as Epimetheus had given the other animals. To help the poor creature at all, Prometheus would have to resort to unusual means. What one gift could he find for man, to save him and even make him superior to the animals?

Prometheus had seen the sacred fire, kindled by the sun-god, which burned on Mount Olympus. He realized that if mankind could obtain this unique possession, he would not only survive but would be able to raise himself far above the animals and eventually develop the civilizations which Prometheus foresaw.

In the depth of the night, when all the gods were asleep, Prometheus crept to the shrine on Mount Olympus; stealthily, he lighted a hollow reed at the sacred fire, and quickly made his way down the mountainside to the place where the frightened men awaited him.

Zeus was furious to see so powerful an instrument of progress in the hands of unworthy mortals, for this would allow man to warm his house, to cook his food, and to shape his weapons and utensils out of metal. But his fury knew no bounds when the Titan deceived him a second time.

Prometheus had been asked to decide which portions of sacrificial bull should be taken by Zeus and the Olympians, and which should be retained by the sacrificers. He decided to trick Zeus by having him choose between two portions. One appeared to be rich, nourishing meat, but was really only a pile of bare bones covered by deceptive fat; the other seemed a mess of disgusting entrails, but under it was hidden the good meat. Zeus greedily chose the attractive, glistening fat. He realized his mistake almost at once, but the decision was binding and he could do nothing about it. For all time, man was to keep the tasty parts of a sacrifice for himself, and give the gods only the useless bones.

The third and final outrage came when Prometheus refused to give Zeus the one secret which he desperately wanted to know—the secret of the Fates, the three sisters who spun, drew out, and cut the thread of life. The sisters had informed Prometheus that one day Zeus would have a son who would overthrow him. When Zeus realized that Prometheus would never acknowledge his authority by revealing the secret to him, he devised the most horrible punishment conceivable for the renegade. The king of the gods banished Prometheus to the far-off, craggy Caucasus mountains, there to be stretched on the highest rock, chained for eternity. Every day he was to suffer terrible torment, for Zeus sent an eagle to tear interminably at the Titan's liver. His torture was to be endless, for nightly the parts the eagle had torn away from his body were renewed.

Prometheus' beloved mankind lived on to benefit from the gifts of the suffering Titan.

IN HISTORY

It is not difficult to see why the early Greeks invented the story of Prometheus, for the discovery of fire was the most important event in the history of mankind.

Almost every animal which has survived to the present age has some natural means of protection against its enemies—speed, toughness of hide, great size, protective colouring, and so on. As is illustrated by the Prometheus-Epimetheus creation story, mankind lacked these natural advantages possessed by the lesser animals.

Man's only natural protection is his superior brain capacity, which led him quickly to the discovery that fire could keep away predatory animals, as well as giving him warmth. No one knows how primitive man "captured" fire—perhaps he saw the flames of a lightning-struck tree or dry grass that had been ignited by some natural phenomenon—but men soon sought an explanation. The story of a god who was their champion, stealing a sacred flame from the home of the gods themselves, was their answer.

* * *

The story of the sacrifice decision is an attempt to justify the old Greek practice of sacrificing only the thigh-bones and certain other parts to the gods. The meat was kept by the men as a matter of economy.

ECHOES IN LITERATURE

The great Greek dramatist Aeschylus was probably the first to adopt Prometheus as the subject of powerful literary works. Apparently he wrote a pair of plays called *Prometheus Bound* and *Prometheus Unbound,* using the Titan as a symbol for mankind; the second play, however, has been lost.

Quite a number of English-speaking poets similarly used the figure of Prometheus as a symbol. Byron's *Prometheus* advances the idea that the Titan gave man his spark of intellect, as well as setting the example of refusal to give in to defeat in death. Shelley, a poet living at the same time as Byron, presented an even more elevated portrait of the Titan. In *Prometheus Unbound,* a poetic drama, he painted Zeus as evil, and Prometheus as having the power to help mankind find its way back to a state of innocence; Prometheus refuses to tell Zeus the secret which would allow him to stay strong forever, and when Zeus is finally overthrown, Prometheus is freed by Heracles, representing strength.

Other poets have interpreted Prometheus to represent the spirit of poetry, religion, and other expressions of the human soul.

PANDORA

I F Zeus had not heaped bitter revenge upon Prometheus and the race of mortals he had befriended, the world might still be a happy place.

Zeus perceived that he could best hurt the Titan rebel by inflicting suffering upon the race of mortals he loved. He knew, too, that Prometheus had tried to protect mankind forever by catching all the evils and spites which could exist on the earth and imprisoning them in one great jar. They could never escape from this jar by themselves, and it was guarded by Prometheus' brother Epimetheus, who, although not wise like his brother, had been carefully warned to keep the jar tightly closed forever and was faithfully keeping watch over it.

The scheme of Zeus was to send a woman to Epimetheus to be his companion and wife. Hephaestus, the smith of Olympus, fashioned her, and made her features and form lovely as those of any goddess. Each of the other Olympians gave her a special gift to make her attractive, and when the Winds finally breathed life into her, no more beautiful and desirable woman had ever graced the earth. She was named Pandora, which means "gifts of all", as a reminder of the beauties and talents she had been given by all the gods.

Epimetheus had been warned by his brother never to accept any gift from Zeus, but he could not resist the lovely creature sent from heaven, and made her his wife.

Hidden among her gifts, however, was one quality which Zeus had mixed liberally into her nature—curiosity. The king of the gods had planned wisely, for as soon as Pandora laid eyes upon the great jar which Epimetheus guarded, she was seized by an irresistible desire to know what was inside.

"Epimetheus," she said, "what harm could it do if you just took one little peek? After all, you are entitled to know what you're guarding!"

But Epimetheus refused to listen.

"Perhaps there is a treasure inside," Pandora continued. "It must be something wonderful, or your brother would not be having you guard it so carefully!"

Epimetheus shook his head, but Pandora would not be silenced.

"If we only knew, then we could guard it better," she said. "Who knows, perhaps there is nothing in there at all, and your brother is just trying to keep you from spending your time in any other way! Couldn't we take just one look?"

For a long time she pestered her husband, but Epimetheus would not budge. Pandora at last stopped asking, but her thoughts were filled, night and day, waking and sleeping, working or at play, with the mystery of the contents of the jar. Finally she could stand it no longer, and one day when her husband's back was turned, she swept the lid from the jar.

Pandora screamed as dozens of cruel, stinging little spites flew from the jar. In a great cloud they swarmed out, stinging her and Epimetheus in all parts of their bodies before they flew off in all directions. Illness was there, and vice, and fury, labour, madness—all the troubles which have beset the world since that time.

After all the troubles had stung the unhappy Pandora and Epimetheus, one small form fluttered gently from the jar. It was Hope, who alone is able to live with any of the evils. In her soft voice she whispered dreams of the future which were the only balm to help the anguished couple bear their pain.

From the top of Olympus, Zeus laughed gleefully to see the success of his plan, for through the curiosity of one woman he had succeeded in tormenting the race of mortals for all time.

LTHOUGH early men were good and innocent creatures, the passing centuries changed them, and there came a time when the gods looked down in displeasure upon the earth and its inhabitants.

In the iron age, man became subject to all manner of crime, deceit, and treachery. The source of their evil may have been their new knowledge and their material advancement, for when they had learned to take from the earth its hidden stores, they discovered the metal which gave the age its name. With it they learned to make weapons more terrible than any that had been known before, so that violence and bloodshed became commonplace. Even more terrible was the discovery of another metal, gold: from it men learned greed and desire, the motives for fighting and killing. The earth and its riches had once belonged to all, but as men learned to value possessions, the land itself was divided up and people fought for pieces of it. Some men lived by plunder, sparing not even their own brothers and sons in their search for wealth. All the old virtues which men had once possessed seemed to be dead.

From the heights of Mount Olympus, Zeus and his brothers looked down on the depravity of mankind, and the king of the gods sadly addressed his family.

"I have loved these creatures and I have delighted to see them, but now they have dedicated themselves to crime and evil. All must be punished. The race of mortals must be wiped from the face of the earth."

Dreadful as were these words, the rest of the gods knew that Zeus was right. There seemed no other way to bring the world back to the goodness and innocence it had once known. All were grieved, however, at the idea of a world without people, and questioned Zeus about the future.

19

"Never fear," he said. "I have made provision for a new race, a finer one than that which now exists."

With this assurance, the gods set out to assist Zeus in his awesome plan for destruction. The king of the gods first shut up the north wind in the caves of Aeolus, and set loose the south wind whose beard is heavy with rain. Sheets of water poured from the heavens, rain such as the world had never known and has never known since. The crops of the farmers were devastated, and even their houses were battered by the rain.

At the same time, Poseidon released the rivers from their banks and struck the earth with his trident. Great cracks appeared in the earth itself, and became channels in which new rivers flowed. Water poured over the plains until all the earth was covered; not a house was left standing. Animals were washed away, and seals played where once goats had grazed. Fishes swam among the topmost branches of the trees. Birds circled above the waves, seeking a landing place until, overcome by exhaustion, they fell into the sea and drowned.

One of the men who attempted to survive by building a boat to float upon the waves was Deucalion, the son of Prometheus. He and his wife, Pyrrha, the daughter of Epimetheus, were both good and upright, and because of their goodness they were spared. When their little boat came to rest on the twin peaks of Mount Parnassus, in Phocis, the first action of the two mortals was to offer prayers to certain of the nymphs and gods.

Zeus looked down from heaven and saw the two praying mortals, sole survivors of the waves which covered the whole of the earth. He knew them to be true worshippers, and was satisfied that all guilty men had been destroyed; since his task was accomplished, he released the North Wind from its prison and allowed it to drive back the clouds that surrounded the earth. Great Poseidon summoned from the depths of the water the sea-god Triton, who arose wreathed with shellfish and holding his coiling conch-shell trumpet. He put the trumpet to his lips and blew the notes which were a signal to all the waters to retreat. They rushed back to their natural bounds, the sea to its bed and the rivers to the confines of their banks. Gradually the earth reappeared, although mud and silt still clung to the branches of the trees and all lands were desolate and silent.

Deucalion and Pyrrha, the lone survivors, appealed to the Titaness

Themis for advice, for they wished to do everything in their power to repair the desolation. The goddess took pity on them, and uttered these words:

"Depart from my temple, veil your heads, loosen the girdles of your garments, and throw behind you the bones of your great mother."

After pondering this message, Deucalion decided that the goddess meant that they were to throw behind them stones which they picked up from their great mother, the earth. They doubted that such action could accomplish anything, but hesitated to disregard the oracles of a goddess; so, strange as the advice sounded, they followed it.

Deucalion and Pyrrha picked up handfuls of stones and tossed them behind as they walked. Then the plan of the gods was made clear, for the stones began, mysteriously, to lose their hardness and soften into new shapes. They grew, and the stony parts became bones, the earth-covered parts flesh; veins in the stones became veins in the body, and eventually the stones thrown by Deucalion grew into men and those thrown by his wife into women.

Thus the new race of men was created from the earth.

Later, as the sun's rays warmed the mud, animals of many kinds were created from the combination of the elements of heat and moisture. Before long the animals which we know today, as well as many marvellous creatures that lived only in ancient times, populated the earth.

In this way the gods destroyed all of the earth's old, evil life, and tried to bring the world back to its original beauty and innocence.

IN HISTORY

The story of Deucalion is not the only account of a flood which swept over the world, wiping out almost all life. In fact, a similar flood story is contained in the mythologies of a great number of peoples. The stories are astonishingly similar even in their details; for example, the deluge is sent by the gods (or a god) to punish the human race for its sins; one family manages to survive because of their virtue. They build a boat of certain measurements and float upon the waves for many days before coming to rest upon a mountaintop.

The story seems to have spread to the Greeks, to the Hebrews, and to other peoples from the Sumerians of Mesopotamia. For centuries people argued about the story: had there ever been a flood? If so, did it cover the whole earth? When did it occur? Was all life wiped out, so that the world had to be repopulated afterwards?

Records discovered in Mesopotamia tended to support the myth of the flood. However, like many early records, they were fantastically inaccurate, and failed to answer any of the questions. A list of kings which had been drawn up about 4,000 years ago by Sumerian scribes divides the kings into those who ruled before "the Flood" and those who came after, but since it assigns to eight kings reigns which totalled 241,200 years, no one took it very seriously.

In 1929, however, a startling discovery was made by Sir Leonard Woolley, director of excavations at the site of the ancient city of Ur. A pit dug at a certain spot revealed the usual record of civilization—ashes, potsherds, and the like—for some feet. Then, suddenly, the diggers came upon a layer of pure silt, containing no records of civilization, only clean, water-laid mud. Convinced that they had reached virgin soil, the diggers wanted to stop; Woolley, however, had calculated that the virgin soil should lie deeper, and insisted they continue digging. To their astonishment, after they had dug through about eight feet of mud they came upon a new layer containing the refuse of ancient peoples.

The layer of silt was clear evidence of some tremendous flood that had swept the Mesopotamian plain. Microscopic analysis proved the mud to be water-laid, and its placement proved that people had lived on the land before the mud was deposited, and again afterwards, all within civilized times. At its thickest, the layer of mud measured eleven feet, which, Woolley calculated, meant that the waters must have been at least twenty-five feet deep. (The account of Noah's flood in *Genesis* says the waters measured fifteen cubits, or twenty-one to twenty-six feet.) The plain is extremely low, Ur itself, two hundred miles from the sea, being only fourteen feet above sea level; a twenty-five foot flood would drown an area at least three hundred miles long and one hundred wide. Only a few major cities, built on mounds, would survive. The villages would be swept away.

A villager who managed to build some sort of boat and save his family would, Sir Leonard Woolley concluded, be justly regarded as a hero upon whom the gods looked with special favour.

ECHOES IN LITERATURE

English writers, like those of many nations, have remarked upon the similarities of the Deucalion story to the Biblical story of Noah. Three and a half centuries ago, Giles Fletcher demanded in *Christ's Victorie and Triumph in Heaven and Earth*:

> Who doth not see drown'd in Deucalion's name
> (When earth his men, and sea had lost his shore)
> Old Noah . . . ?

THE OLYMPIAN FAMILY

Like the Greeks, the Romans developed a set of deities who ruled over specific fields. About the third century B.C., the Greeks and Romans began to assume that their deities were actually the same, merely called by different names. In many cases, the Latin names are more familiar to us.

The following lists show the Latin deities corresponding to the best-known Greek ones.

Cronus—Saturn
Rhea—Ops
Gaea—Tellus
Zeus—Jupiter
Hera—Juno
Athene—Minerva
Apollo—Apollo
Artemis—Diana
Ares—Mars

Aphrodite—Venus
Hephaestus—Vulcan
Eros—Cupid
Poseidon—Neptune
Hades—Pluto
Hestia—Vesta
Demeter—Ceres
Dionysus—Bacchus
Persephone—Proserpina

THE OLYMPIAN FAMILY

ITH the defeat and banishment of the Titans, Zeus and his family became rulers of the universe.

Among the brothers Zeus, Hades, and Poseidon were divided the sky, the underworld, and the sea. The land was supposed to be ruled by all the members of the family, none having more influence than any other; actually, though, since Zeus was considered the king of the gods, he was revered by men too as the supreme ruler.

With the exception of unsocial Hades, who preferred his own dark realms, the gods went to live on Mount Olympus. From this vantage point they could see the doings of all men, and each assumed the charge of certain fields of activity.

Hera, acknowledged queen of heaven because of her marriage to Zeus, was also a daughter of Cronus and Rhea. She was born at Samos, an island which has since been sacred to her, and was nursed through childhood by the Seasons.

She was the most majestic of the goddesses, very tall and fair-skinned, with an exalted, severe beauty. Some claim that she did not want to marry Zeus, and rejected him several times before he tricked her into giving her affection by coming to her disguised as a spring-heralding bird. She finally accepted him, and their wedding was one of the greatest events to take place on Mount Olympus. Hera was presented with all manner of wonderful gifts by other gods and goddesses, but her favourite of them all was a tree which bore apples of pure gold, the gift of Earth. The magic tree grew in a special garden at the western end of the Mediterranean, where it was guarded by the sweet-singing Hesperides, daughters of Night.

Her married life was not a happy one, for Zeus, the most unfaithful of husbands, had an eye that could be caught by any goddess or lovely mortal. He had almost no idea of fidelity, while Hera, on the other hand, was so strictly moral that she became the protectress of honourable marriage. Their constant bickering became a laughing matter on earth as well as on Olympus; but Hera's powers were not equal to those of Zeus, and she often had to use low tricks to humiliate Zeus and thwart his schemes of infidelity. As might be expected, passing time made her more and more jealous, guileful, and cruel.

When she appeared to mortals, Hera could usually be identified by her height, her white arms and lovely hair, and by the cuckoo, messenger of spring, which was always with her.

ECHOES IN LITERATURE

Hera is renowned for her absolute virtue, which has been praised by many English poets. Spenser, for example, invoked her blessing on his own marriage in the wedding poem *Epithalamion*.

In terms of the reverence paid by mortals, Athene was probably second only to Zeus among the Olympians.

There are many tales of her birth. According to the most common, she was the daughter of Zeus and a Titaness named Metis, whose name means "wise counsel." Before the child was born, Zeus began to fear that the combination of his strength and Metis' wisdom might produce a son who was stronger than his father. Though anxious to dispose of Metis immediately, he was reluctant to lose her wise counsel. His solution was ingenious; he swallowed the Titaness whole, and ever afterwards claimed that she advised him from within.

Some time later, Zeus developed a headache so agonizing that he felt as if his whole skull were going to split—which it eventually did. From his brain sprang forth, fully armed, the goddess Athene.

Thankful that she was not a son, Zeus handed her over to the care of Triton, a sea and river god.

Throughout childhood, Athene always seemed more like a boy than a girl. Her games with her little companion, Pallas, daughter of the river god, were all of war and fighting. During one of these games she accidentally struck Pallas a heavy blow with her javelin, and the girl was killed. Athene was so remorseful that she placed her friend's name before her own, and asked to be known as Pallas Athene.

Her lack of femininity was further revealed in the spheres over which she chose to rule. She became the goddess of war, although she did not share the love of blood that the war god, Ares, exhibited; she often insisted that she preferred her other function, the goddess of wisdom and justice.

Athene benefited mankind by inventing for them such necessities as the plough, the ship, the pot, and the yoke, and gained such respect that the citizens of Greece's greatest city, Athens, adopted her as their patron, named the city after her, and in her honour built the Parthenon which crowns their highest hill.

IN HISTORY

Undoubtedly the most famous Greek temple was the Parthenon, which crowns the Acropolis in Athens. It was built at the order of Pericles, and finished about 438

B.C. The sculptor Phidias, who participated in the work himself, directed the sculptures in the pediments and the magnificent frieze.

Originally dedicated to Athene, the Parthenon became in medieval days a Christian church and later a Moslem mosque. Seventeenth-century Turks used it to store explosives during a war with Venice, and in 1687 the temple was blown up.

In the nineteenth century, Lord Elgin removed most of the surviving sculptures to the British Museum in London. At the present time, there is a movement to have the Elgin Marbles restored to Greece.

APHRODITE

Very different from Athene was Aphrodite, the goddess of love. Born from the foam of the sea, she floated upon a scallop shell, first to the island of Cythera, which she judged to be too small for her home, and then to Cyprus.

Aphrodite, loveliest of all the goddesses, was accompanied on her wanderings by the doves which have since become symbols of tender romance. She held as her most precious charm a magic belt or girdle which made mortals fall in love with whoever happened to be wearing it. She in turn was attracted to a great number of men.

Ironically, this most beautiful of the goddesses was married to the ugliest of gods, Hephaestus, and she spent much of her time in the company of others. Her favourite was Ares, the god of war; however, she was known to have been in love, at various times, with Hermes, Poseidon, Dionysus, and other gods.

Several of her mortal lovers achieved lasting fame. One was Anchises, a shepherd who foolishly admitted to his friends that he had won the love of a goddess. Zeus heard his words and tried to strike him dead with a blow of the thunderbolt, but Aphrodite jumped to protect her lover at the last moment, so that he was only crippled. The son of Aphrodite and Anchises was Aeneas, who led a band of Trojans to found the city of Rome.

Another of her loves was Adonis, the most beautiful youth in the world.

POSEIDON AND HADES

Poseidon, though ruler of the sea, was very much at home on Olympus with the rest of the family, and spent most of his time there. Still, clad in a golden robe and driving wild-maned horses, he would occasionally set out over his domain. With his trident which could shatter the earth and stir up the sea, Poseidon would sometimes cause huge storms to shake the whole earth. Just as quickly, then, he would bring calm.

Hades, on the other hand, hardly ever left his underworld kingdom to come to Olympus. He was not liked by the rest of the gods, and he frightened some of the goddesses.

IN HISTORY

Poseidon was supposed to have been particularly fond of the horse, perhaps because of the resemblance of breaking waves to snowy manes. A devoutly-observed ritual in ancient Greece was the ceremony performed at the still-standing temple of Poseidon at Cape Sunium in Attica, where horses were cast off a cliff and into the sea as a gift for Poseidon. He was, of course, one of the most popular gods in Greece, for the Greeks were a sea-faring people, and thus had to keep Poseidon's favour at all times.

APOLLO

Honoured by the Greeks immediately after Zeus and Athene was the god Apollo.

Apollo was the son of Zeus and a Titaness named Leto, who was accorded the privileges of an Olympian. He had a twin sister, born just before him—Artemis, famous in her own right.

When Apollo was only four days old, his mother took him to the island of Delphi, where lived her enemy, a huge and terrible dragon called the Python. As soon as he caught sight of the serpent, Apollo shot arrow after arrow into its long, coiling body; he sensed that he must be his mother's champion. Then he sang a paean of victory over its limp carcass.

The island where the serpent had lived became sacred to Apollo, and it was there that an oracle (called Pythia, after the Python) uttered the most renowned prophecies of ancient times.

Some of the gods considered that Apollo had committed a murder by killing the Python, and they sent him to do penance by serving a certain King Admetus of Therae for eight years. His services won the king's undying gratitude. On one occasion, he helped the king win his beloved Alcestis to wife by performing the seemingly impossible task of yoking together a lion and a boar. On another, he saved the king from his destined death by tricking the Fates with strong liquor.

In another version of the story, Apollo did penance for his rage after the death of his son Asclepius, god of medicine.

After serving the penance, Apollo was so changed that he became the advocate of moderation in all things. He learned the use of the lyre, and played so beautifully that he was regarded as the god of music. Greeks identified his goodness with the brightness of the sun, and honoured him as the sun-god under the name Phoebus Apollo.

Despite his fine qualities, Apollo could on occasion be very cruel. This defect in his character was revealed in his dealings with women whom he loved but who rejected him.

One, Cassandra, was a princess of Troy. To win her, Apollo bestowed upon her the gift of prophecy; she still failed to love him, and Apollo could not take back the gift once given. In his anger, he put a curse upon Cassandra: as promised, she would be able to foretell the future, but no one would ever believe her words. In later years Cassandra tried to warn the people of Troy of their doom, but everyone only laughed at her. Still later, she foresaw her own death.

Another woman who suffered Apollo's anger for rejection of his advances was the Sibyl of Cumae, a prophetess who lived on the west coast of Italy. When Apollo had asked her to name the gift she wanted, she had said, "Let me live as long as there are grains of sand in that dune," indicating a great heap of sand tossed up by the sea. Apollo granted the wish, but when she rejected him, he made sure that the Sibyl grew old at the same time as other mortals, so that she had to spend countless ages as an old, old woman.

Another maiden whom Apollo loved, the graceful nymph Daphne, prayed to be saved from the advances of the god, and as she fled from him she was transformed into a laurel tree. Apollo was so moved by the loss that he made the laurel tree one of his sacred symbols.

However, Apollo was not always the one whose love was rejected. Clytie, a mortal girl, loved him so dearly that she could not take her eyes from him as he drove his flaming chariot across the sky. Finally, Apollo took pity on her and changed her into a flower, the heliotrope, whose blossom turns to follow the sun's progress across the sky.

Other plants, too, owe their origin to Apollo. The flower which the Greeks call the hyacinth was created from the blood of Hyacinthus, a boy whom Apollo regarded as his best friend. While the god and his friend were practising tossing the discus, Apollo accidentally struck Hyacinthus in the forehead, wounding him fatally. Upon the petals of the purple mourning-flower are inscribed the Greek syllables for a wail of lamentation, to commemorate the grief of Apollo.

A boy named Cyparissus had a pet stag, which he killed by mistake. His prayer that Apollo let him mourn forever was answered by his being turned into the gloomy, mournful cypress tree.

IN HISTORY

The development of the concept of justice and punishment among the Greeks is reflected in the story of Apollo. Among early peoples justice often took the form of vengeance, usually taken by the offended person or his family on the offender. The concept is illustrated by the saying "An eye for an eye, and a tooth for a tooth."

More advanced people sometimes developed the concept of atonement, whereby a guilty person could be cleansed by doing penance for his crime. Among the Greeks, penance apparently often took the form of serving another person for a specified time, and carrying out that person's every wish. In the story of Apollo's penance we find the earliest Greek reference to atonement.

29

ECHOES IN LITERATURE

Apollo is frequently invoked in English literature as the patron of poetry, although poetic use of his name often refers simply to the sun.

The god is the hero of Keats' unfinished work, *Hyperion*. In the poem, he is shown as representing knowledge and self-control, the qualities which would be necessary for man's spiritual progress.

In *The Last Oracle*, Swinburne addresses Apollo as the one enduring god:

> Thou the word, the light, the life, the breath, the glory,
> Strong to help and heal, to lighten and to slay. . . .

ARTEMIS

Apollo's twin sister was Artemis, the huntress. Artemis had the strength of a boy, and a boy's love of the outdoors; her greatest enjoyment was drawn from the chase. Strangely, though, she could be gentle, and all animals too young to look after themselves, and children, too, were taken under her special protection.

Artemis was renowned as goddess of the moon, and was regarded as the protector of young maidens.

The chaste Artemis was extremely modest. One day she set aside her saffron hunting tunic with its scarlet hem to bathe in a stream, and discovered that she had been seen by a hunter, Actaëon. In rage, Artemis turned the luckless Actaëon into a stag, and his own pack of fifty hounds tore him to pieces.

She demanded the same high standards of modesty from the young maidens who sought to be her companions. On one occasion she found cause to suspect that one of her followers, Callisto, had not been virtuous, and immediately changed the girl into a bear. The hounds of Artemis would have attacked Callisto had not Zeus, at the last moment, picked her up and set her among the stars.

Only once did Artemis fall in love. She happened to see a shepherd, Endymion, sleeping on the mountain, and was so captivated by his appearance that she came down to kiss him. So that she might always love and yet never lose her modesty, Artemis gave Endymion eternal youth and eternal sleep, and often descended from the sky to watch him as he slumbered.

ECHOES IN LITERATURE

The popularity of Artemis in literature has more than one foundation.

The story of her love for Endymion is extremely popular among poets, and references to it are numerous. Three poets, Lyly and Drayton in Elizabethan times, and Keats two centuries later, developed the theme into long poetic works in which the goddess is used as a symbol. Keats, for example, used the story to illustrate the truth that divine love could be achieved only through living here on earth, and feeling human love.

Because of her virtue, Artemis was often used as a symbol of beauty of the spirit. Even more popular, particularly among writers of about the time of Shakespeare, were references to her as the goddess of the moon. Often calling her by her Latin name Diana, or sometimes Cynthia, poets appealed to her for assistance or proclaimed to her their undying love. Sometimes she represented the Queen, Elizabeth I, whose favour many poets of the period sought and found. One of the best examples of identification of the queen with the goddess is Ben Jonson's short poem, "Hymn to Diana."

ARES

Ares and his twin sister Eris were children of Zeus and Hera, and were the most warlike of all the Olympians. Eris was restricted to meddling and quarrel-causing, but Ares became the god of war and delighted in violent and bloody battle. His bloodthirstiness was so terrible that it brought to Ares the hatred of all the gods and goddesses, even his own parents. The sole exception was Aphrodite, who was enamoured by his strong, straight-limbed form.

Ares never favoured one side consistently in a battle; instead, he usually tried to prolong conflict by helping first one force, then the other. Many brave men died needlessly to satisfy Ares' blood-lust.

31

HESTIA

Hestia, a daughter of Cronus and Rhea, was one of the elder Olympians. Both Hades and Poseidon had wanted to marry her, but she had refused them and taken a vow that she would never marry anyone. Zeus was so impressed by his sister's vow that he decreed that she was to be worshipped in every home on earth.

Hestia became the goddess of the hearth, and her fire was considered as sacred in the home as in a temple. No unworthy deed was to be done within view of Hestia's symbolic flame; no child could be received into the family before it had been carried around it; and every meal both began and ended with a prayer to Hestia, the protector of the home.

IN HISTORY

Although the goddess Hestia plays almost no part in the myths, she was one of the most important deities.

Each city in ancient Greece lit a flame to Hestia, and the fire was never allowed to go out. Colonists in the sixth century B.C. and before carried coals from the mother city to start Hestia's flame in their new home.

Hestia is associated almost as much as Zeus with the law of hospitality ordained by the king of the gods. The Greeks believed that a sacred bond existed between host and guest: the host was bound by the sacred law to receive a guest with all good will, and the guest for his part was bound to respect his host and do his bidding.

In Rome, Hestia was known as Vesta, and was the most important of the Roman goddesses. She was worshipped in much the same manner as in Greece, but the family's sacred hearth took on even greater significance in Rome. One of the city's most important shrines was the temple where Vesta's flame was tended by priestesses known as Vestal virgins, and the duties of these maidens were considered so sacred that a girl who broke her vows was beaten or even buried alive.

HEPHAESTUS

Hephaestus, son of Zeus and Hera, was the only one of the Olympians who did not enjoy beauty of appearance. At birth he was so small, sickly, and deformed that he filled even his mother with disgust, and to escape the mockery of the other goddesses, she tossed him off Mount Olympus. Luckily, he landed in the sea, and the nymphs looked after him in a cavern running far under the land. In that secret cavern he learned the arts of metal-work, and the objects he produced were so beautiful that eventually he was summoned back to Olympus.

There he set up his forge and fashioned wonderful weapons and ornaments for the gods, and even married the loveliest of the goddesses, Aphrodite. On one occasion, though, he interfered in a quarrel between his parents by taking Hera's side, and Zeus became so angry that he threw Hephaestus a second time from Olympus. This time he landed on solid earth and broke both legs. He was a cripple thereafter.

Hephaestus' ill-tempered ugliness and Aphrodite's wandering affections proved a bad combination. Jealous of her many loves, he tried several times to shame his wife publicly, but the sympathies of most of the gods remained with the beautiful goddess instead of with her outraged husband. He won the admiration of all, however, by the matchless beauty of his metal-work.

HERMES

Hermes, another son of Zeus, first became famous for his skill in stealing, and has been the patron of thieves ever since.

While only one day old, Hermes stole a herd of cows from Apollo and hid their tracks by shoeing each one with slippers of bark and grass. Prudently, he sacrificed two of the cattle to the gods, taking it for granted that he was included in the list of deities; he invented the lyre, which he fashioned with strips of cowhide and the shell of a tortoise; then he gave the instrument to Apollo to assuage his wrath.

Some time later, he made another musical instrument from reeds, and traded this with Apollo, taking in exchange the god's golden staff. For this, he became the patron of merchants and traders.

His most important role, however, was that of Zeus' herald and messenger of the gods. To travel quickly from place to place, he wore winged golden sandals which bore him through the air, and a winged helmet to protect him against foul weather.

In spite of the trust he was accorded by Zeus, Hermes never lost his guile, and remained one of the most fun-loving, trick-playing, and charming of the gods.

EROS

A god who was much older than the Olympians was Eros, god of love. He was welcomed into their company, and played a great part in the loves and marriages of both gods and mortals.

Some stories, however, claimed that Eros was really the son of Aphrodite. For this reason, he is often pictured as a child or a very young man, armed with the bows and arrows which make mortals fall in love.

DEMETER

Demeter was the goddess of the fields and crops, and is best known through the story of her grief for her daughter Persephone, who was stolen away to become queen of the underworld.

Demeter sent a serpent-drawn chariot to all parts of the world so that mankind might be taught the arts of agriculture and the features of civilization that accompany them—settlement, law and order, and marriage.

One of Zeus' secret loves was Semele, a mortal woman. After a time she pleaded to see Zeus in his full glory, and the sight of his radiance destroyed her. However, the god Hermes managed to save Semele's unborn child, and sewed him up in the thigh of Zeus. When the child was born from the thigh, he was named Dionysus, sometimes called "the twice-born."

Dionysus was renowned for the invention of wine. With his debauched old tutor, Silenus, he travelled the world; wherever men received him with courtesy, they received the vine and the knowledge of its cultivation, but where they turned Dionysus away, they were punished severely.

IN HISTORY

The worship of Dionysus attracted a great number of followers, some of whom committed outrageous deeds as part of their rituals.

There was a story in which Dionysus was said to have been torn to pieces as a child, and was reborn after spending three years in Hades. To commemorate this tale, female worshippers of the god met every third year to re-enact the death and rebirth of the god. The rites, intended to express their grief at his death and joy at his rebirth, became extremely savage. The women would roam the forests and fields, drums beating and flutes playing a wild tune, and would work themselves into a frenzy: they twined ivy or even snakes in their hair, performed wild ritualistic dances, and fell upon any wild creature they met, tore it to pieces, and ate it raw in imitation of the cruel death of the god. They were widely known by names which suggest their raging madness, Bacchae or Maenads.

Other rituals, less gory but no less wild, were held by tribes and villages in honour of the god's role in the crop-producing fertility of the earth. Though they were at first little more than orgies, the rituals performed gradually became more and more clearly defined, and over many centuries developed into the earliest form of drama.

ECHOES IN LITERATURE

Dionysus appears frequently in English poetry, usually under his Roman name Bacchus. Short poems were written in his honour, seeing him as the god of revelry and earthly pleasures.

Reference to his flirtation with Aphrodite are common. The lovers are usually called by the Latin Venus and Bacchus.

Bacchanalia, or festivals of revelry, are treated in various ways by the poets. Many reject them as pagan debaucheries, but a few interpret them as outpourings of poetic inspiration.

LESSER DEITIES

Sharing the company of the great and powerful gods were less important ones, among them Iris, the rainbow-goddess who often acted as a messenger; Hebe, goddess of youth; Ganymede, the personal cup-bearer of Zeus; and the Graces and Muses.

The Muses were the nine daughters of Zeus and Mnemosyne, whose name means memory. At first they were goddesses of song, but later they divided the whole field of poetry, arts, and sciences among them. Although their home was on Mount Parnassus, they entertained the Olympians at their banquets by their sweet song.

Calliope, the noblest, was the Muse of epic poetry; Clio, of history; Euterpe, of lyric poetry; Thalia, of comedy and pastoral poetry; Melpomene, of tragedy; Terpsichore, of dancing; Erato, of love poetry; Polyhymnia, of sacred poetry and hymns, and Urania, the Muse of astronomy.

The Graces, whose names meant Splendour, Laughter, and Good Cheer, were three lovely daughters of Zeus whose presence always brought happiness.

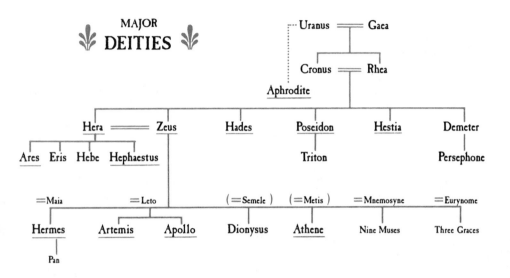

MAJOR DEITIES

Uranus === Gaea

Cronus === Rhea

Aphrodite

Hera === Zeus   Hades   Poseidon   Hestia   Demeter

Ares Eris Hebe Hephaestus   Triton   Persephone

=Maia   =Leto   (=Semele) (=Metis)   =Mnemosyne   =Eurynome

Hermes   Artemis   Apollo   Dionysus   Athene   Nine Muses   Three Graces

Pan

Deities whose names are underlined are referred to as the Twelve Great Olympians.

Nemesis was a goddess who played an important role in the lives of men. She believed in rewarding the good and punishing the guilty exactly in accordance with their own deeds, and mortals often prayed to her to judge their fellows.

ECHOES IN LITERATURE

More references are made to the Muses in English poetry than to any other classical beings, for poets frequently have called upon them, individually or collectively, for inspiration.

One of the greatest works of the language, Milton's *Paradise Lost*, begins with an invocation to the Muse to help the poet with his story of the fall of man. Milton thus turned the pagan Muse to a Christian use.

37

GODS AND MONSTERS

Many other creatures of wonder lived at the same time as the Olympian gods, but did not share their dwelling on Mount Olympus.

Even Zeus himself lived in awe of the Fates, three daughters of Night who lived in a heavenly cave by a pool of gleaming white water, for they alone had the power of determining when each man's death day would fall. Quietly they sat by their gleaming pool, one spinning the thread of life, one measuring it, and the third cutting it with her shears when life was to end. The Fates were remorseless, caring nothing for the circumstances of a man's life: when they decided he should die, they simply cut the thread of his life.

A god who never gained much respect from the others was disreputable old Pan, who had the horns and hooves of a goat. He was the guardian of flocks and herds in rural Arcadia, and his life was one of ease and pleasure. Although the nymphs and maidens whom he pursued almost always repulsed him, disgusted by his goat-like appearance, all mortals were entranced by the sweet songs he played on his pipes, and there was widespread mourning when he died—the only god who ever did.

The pipes that Pan played were actually once a lovely woodland nymph named Syrinx. To rescue her from Pan's embraces, the gods changed Syrinx into reeds growing upon the bank of a stream. Pan could still hear in their murmur, as the wind passed over them, the soft, melodious voice of his beloved, and he determined that she should sing forever. He bound the reeds into a musical instrument, which gave to the fields and woodlands the haunting music associated with Pan.

Associated with Pan and with the god Dionysus were a race of beings known as satyrs. They were spirits of the woodland, hairy, goat-eared, and short-tailed, and their interests centred around only three things—wine, women, and roguish pranks.

Their female counterparts in the woodland were the nymphs, whose nature was much finer than that of the satyrs. These lovely maidens won the love of god and mortal alike for both their beauty and their gentleness.

Other strange beings of Greek myth were the Centaurs. They had the torso, arms, and head of a man growing from the body and legs of a horse, and so combined the cunning of man with the horse's strength and speed. Generally, they were regarded as wild, crude, and unfit for human company; however, one of them, Cheiron, was renowned throughout the world for his kindness and wisdom.

ECHOES IN LITERATURE

One popular tradition in English poetry is the **pastoral convention,** in which an idealized rural world of shepherds and shepherdesses is depicted. Often the poems are allegorical, that is, each figure, place, and circumstance is intended to represent something else.

Pan, as the guardian of flocks, figures largely in such poetry. Sometimes he appears as the protector of the fields and woods, sometimes as a symbol of God protecting his people, and sometimes even as the symbol of the universe.

Nymphs and satyrs, too, are frequently used symbolically. Nymphs often represent beautiful women or other lovely, gentle creatures, while satyrs are just the opposite; they represent crudeness, brutality, and uncontrolled passion.

The idea of the three Fates has captured the imagination of countless writers. One of the most common images in literature is that of the thread of life, so fragile that it can be snapped or cut without warning. The idea that the destiny of each man is controlled by remote beings has appealed to many poets.

The three witches or "weird sisters" in *Macbeth* are sometimes considered to be modelled on the Fates, but Shakespeare probably drew his conception of them from the familiar medieval witch. His sisters only foretell the future; they do not control it.

Most modern philosophy has popularized the concept of free will, and consequently writers have generally seen the Fates, or predestination, as evil. Byron in *Manfred* makes the Fates somewhat like the witches of *Macbeth*. In *Apollo and the Fates*, Browning has the goddesses express a belief that life is basically blank and evil, and man merely a puppet for the sport of the Fates.

Several modern writers, including the Victorian novelist Thomas Hardy and the popular twentieth-century writer John O'Hara (*Appointment in Samarra*) express the idea that man is nothing but a plaything in the hands of fate, helpless to be or do anything beyond what has been ordained for him.

BEINGS OF THE
UNDERWORLD

Hades ruled an immense realm stretching under land and sea. His subjects were the dead, but certain immortal creatures lived among them.

The whole realm was divided into several parts, and could be reached from earth through certain caves hidden amid groves of black poplars. Five rivers separated it from the land of the living, and the entering soul had first to be ferried across the river Styx by the ferryman Charon. Anyone who tried to cheat the old miser out of his fare would be captured by Cerberus, the three-headed Hound of Hell who let all souls enter but none leave.

The whole region was sometimes called Tartarus, but the name actually referred to one particular section, the place of torment for evil souls. Another region, called Elysium, was kept for the virtuous, and was a land of happiness where dwelt the souls of those who had achieved good things on earth. Sometimes the souls of heroes went instead to the Isles of the Blest, which were not a part of the underworld at all, but a beautiful place at the end of the world. Those who had been neither good nor bad on earth went to the third section of the underworld, the Asphodel Fields—a cheerless land where wandered dim ghosts who felt neither pain nor pleasure.

Hades and his queen Persephone had their palace in a region called Erebus. There too lived the Erinnyes, or Furies, ancient crones who pursued the guilty on earth, flicking them constantly with whips and allowing them no rest throughout their lives.

The most powerful of all the inhabitants of the underworld was Hecate, a goddess more ancient than any of the Olympians. She was actually a three-fold goddess who had power over the moon, the earth, and the underworld, but it was the underworld that she loved above all. Every night she roamed the earth with the spirits of the dead as her companions, and wherever she went people heard the barking of dogs and the howling of wolves. Many mortals learned the use of

rituals and charms to ward off, and in some cases to win the aid of, the
Mistress of the Underworld.

ECHOES IN LITERATURE

Each of the five rivers of the underworld had a separate character, and literary
references use them symbolically; Styx was the "abhorrent river"; Acheron, the
river of sorrow; Cocytus, of lamentation; Phlegethon, of fire and rage; and Lethe,
the river of forgetfulness or oblivion.

Hecate looms large in literature as the "goddess of the dark of the moon." (She
was sometimes considered to be another aspect of the moon-goddess Artemis.)
Witches and evil beings invoke her; for instance, she is the mistress of the three
witches in *Macbeth*.

BEINGS OF THE SEA

Much more pleasant than the inhabitants of Hades were the creatures
who lived as subjects of Poseidon in the sea or on its shores. There
were many sea-nymphs and lesser gods, among them Triton, who
roused the sea by trumpeting on his coiled conch-shell, and Nereus,
the old man of the sea who could change his form at will. Sometimes
counted, too, as sea-children were the Hesperides, who guarded Hera's
orchard far in the west; the Gorgons, who were once beautiful but
were changed into snake-haired monsters by an angry Athene; the
Graiae or Gray-Haired Women, who were said to be fair even though
they had but one eye and one tooth among them; and the Harpies,
winged creatures who captured mortals and bore them away to unknown lands.

MONSTERS

Of all the monsters that lived in those ancient days, five gained more fame than all the others combined, and they were all from the same family.

The most famous was Cerberus, who guarded the gate of the underworld. He was savage, and had three heads with which to attack; around his three necks grew writhing snakes who sank their poison fangs into anyone who approached. A gentle mortal named Psyche finally learned the secret of calming the rage of Cerberus—she bribed him with bits of cake.

His sister, the Chimaera, lived alone on a mountain-top, from which she sometimes preyed on mortals. She was a combination of lion and goat, with a serpent for a tail, and she breathed fire. Another sister, the Hydra, was a water-serpent with countless heads.

The fourth member of the family was Orthrus, a two-headed hound who was less dreadful and less famous than his daughter, the Sphinx. The Sphinx had the head of a woman set upon the body of a lion, and she gleefully devoured all men who could not answer the riddle she posed: "What walks on four legs in the morning, two at noon, and three at night?" Not until the time of Oedipus, later king of Thebes, was the riddle answered and the Sphinx destroyed.

ECHOES IN LITERATURE

Anyone reading a group of myths and legends chosen at random will doubtless notice the strange similarity among many of them. Several themes are repeated over and over, sometimes differing greatly, sometimes so alike that only the names seem to have been changed.

One such is the theme of the long and perilous voyage. If we were to put the stories of Jason, Odysseus, Aeneas, and parts of the story of Heracles side by side, many incidents would leap out as being closely related. Another is the theme of violent death at the hands of a younger kinsman, which appears several times in the creation stories, and is somehow brought into almost half the myths and legends about mortals.

An extremely popular theme is that of fighting and killing a terrible monster. The god Apollo killed the Python, Theseus the Minotaur, Perseus the Gorgon Medusa, Bellerophon the Chimaera, Oedipus the Sphinx (although indirectly), Heracles all manner of creatures—to mention only a few examples.

Scholars have put forth a variety of interpretations for the popularity of monster-killing stories. Some have claimed them to be merely exaggerations of ordinary hunting exploits: over the centuries, the wolf turns into the invulnerable lion, the snake into the fire-breathing dragon. Others find in them symbols which were used to justify the possession of a throne or position of power by a particular person. Theseus, for instance, appears to have been an early king of Athens, whose power was secured by his killing of the Minotaur, that is, freeing his city from the yoke of Crete. A third theory claims that the stories were inspirational in nature; when the people heard of how one man stood alone against a fearful monster, they would no longer be afraid of the forces which were opposing them. We can imagine how a king or other leader might arrange for a tale of heroes and monsters to be told to his people in times of danger or oppression.

Another interpretation, popular today, is that each monster personified some strong force, usually evil, in the life of early man, and showed that a human could conquer or control such forces.

Whatever the reasons for their origin, such stories will probably strike the reader as quite similar to other stories he has heard; in the fairy-tales told to children, dragons and devouring ogres are among the chief characters. Monster stories, which include even today's "horror" films, appear to have always been among mankind's favourite tales.

THE LOVES OF ZEUS

ZEUS, king of the gods and supreme ruler of mortal men, was not an admirable character. Like many of his family, he was prone to pettiness, jealousy, trickery, and blind rage. Like them, too, he often fell in love with mortals, and his flirtations so roused the wrath of Hera that sometimes there was near-war on Olympus.

Once Zeus had taken notice of a woman, he went to great lengths to win her, resorting if necessary to trickery and disguise. On one famous occasion, Zeus became interested in Alcmene, but knew she was completely devoted to her husband, Amphitryon. Zeus craftily waited until Amphitryon was away, then came to Alcmene in her husband's form. The child of Zeus and Alcmene was the greatest of all heroes, Heracles.

Many times Zeus disguised himself as an animal, in order to approach some unsuspecting maiden. When he fell in love with Europa, for example, he came close to her in the disguise of a white bull, fearsome to see, but gentle as a lamb. Europa was so entranced by the creature that she began to play with him, stroking his ears and winding garlands of vines about his horns, and finally she climbed on his back. There was nothing she could do when the white bull sprang to its feet, dashed off across the meadow and plunged into the sea, bearing his captive to far-off Crete where she could not escape his attentions.

Another beautiful girl, Leda, was enchanted by a white swan which gracefully floated on the river near her home. When she treated him as a pet, he suddenly turned out to be the king of the gods, again in disguise. From this match was born Helen, of Trojan fame.

Sometimes Zeus reversed the disguise trick, changing the maiden into an animal to avoid detection. One such was Io, whom Zeus changed into a white heifer so that she might escape the wrath of Hera. The queen of the goddesses was not deceived, however, and set hundred-eyed Argus to watch over the little cow day and night. When Zeus sent Hermes to bring his love to him, the messenger cut off the head of Argus, and Hera was so horrified by the murder that she set the hundred eyes of Argus in the tail of a peacock, that the world might never forget. Io she punished by forcing her to remain a cow, and she chased her all over the world tortured by a stinging gadfly.

Poor Io roamed over most of Asia and the Near East before finding a home in Egypt where, some say, she was finally restored to human form.

ECHOES IN LITERATURE

English literature abounds with references to the various loves of Zeus, and all his flirtations have been used as the subjects of compositions. One story, however, has been found particularly appealing because of the nature of the disguise assumed by Zeus: the story of the deception of Alcmene. The most recent version is the modern sophisticated comedy by Jean Giradoux, *Amphitryon 38*, which has proved popular in an English translation.

DEMETER AND PERSEPHONE

DEMETER, goddess of the cornfield, had a daughter whom she loved more than any creature in earth or heaven. Her name was Persephone, and she was so lovely that Hades himself sought her hand in marriage.

Zeus, knowing well that Demeter would never consent to the

match and would be furious if he granted permission, suggested instead that Hades might abduct the girl.

Shortly afterwards, as Persephone was picking flowers in the meadow, a great rumbling was heard and the earth at her feet split into a huge, bottomless chasm, Through the gaping split thundered a chariot drawn by four horses black as night, bearing the king of the underworld. Hades snatched the helpless Persephone and carried her down to his dark realm below the earth.

Grief-stricken by her daughter's disappearance, gentle Demeter roamed the earth in search of her. After vain wanderings, she gave a command which she knew would force her daughter's abductors to return her—she stopped all crops from growing. Grain rotted and fruit fell from the vine, and Demeter swore that the earth would remain barren until Persephone returned.

Faced with a starving world, Zeus sent a message to Hades to send the girl back. Although the king of the underworld complied, he announced triumphantly that since Persephone had eaten of the seeds of the pomegranate in his orchard, she had consumed the food of the dead and could never really return to the world of the living.

Finally, Demeter and Hades reached a compromise; Persephone was to spend nine months of the year with her mother, but had to descend to the dark underworld for the other three. So that Hades would never forget his promise, Demeter decreed that the earth would live under a curse of barrenness for the time that Persephone was with him. But for most of the year, she would bless the earth and it would bring forth its crops to feed mankind.

IN HISTORY

Among the places where Demeter searched for her daughter was the city of Eleusis, near Athens. The city became a principal seat of worship of Demeter, and held the Eleusinian Festivals, open to all, and the famed Eleusinian Mysteries. The mysteries, open only to initiates, probably interpreted the annual death and rebirth of Persephone as a symbol of the human spirit's immortality. Their rituals were closely-guarded secrets.

ECHOES IN LITERATURE

The story of Demeter and Persephone is a natural subject for writers, and the story has been retold many times in prose and poetry. Tennyson's *Demeter and Persephone* makes particularly vivid the human emotions of the mother and daughter during the tragedy and the later reunion.

Persephone, in her role as queen of the underworld, has often been portrayed by poets as pale, mysterious, alluring, yet deadly.

PHAETHON

ONE day the fair youth Phaëthon, whose father was the sun-god Apollo, was taunted about his parentage by Epaphus, a youth of the same age whose father was the mighty Zeus.

Stung with shame, Phaëthon reported the insults to his mother Clymene.

"I am unable to answer them. If my father is really a god, as you have told me, give me proof of my noble birth, and let me take my place in heaven."

Clymene was moved.

"It would not take you long to visit your father's dwelling place. If you wish to do so, go and question the sun himself, for Apollo is indeed your father."

Apollo's abode was a lofty palace of glittering gold and bronze. Its towering columns, supporting a roof of polished ivory, shone like fire. Its double doors reflected the light from their silver surfaces.

After climbing the steep approach, Clymene's son was ushered into the presence of his father, who was dressed in a purple robe and was sitting on a throne of shining emeralds. But Phaëthon could not approach too close, for he could not bear the blinding light.

"What do you want in this citadel, Phaëthon, my son? Son, I call you, for you are one whom any parent would be proud to acknowledge."

"To prove that I am indeed your son, give me evidence."

"To remove any doubt from your mind, Phaëthon, make any request you wish, and you shall have it from me."

Instantly the lad asked to be allowed for one day to drive his father's sun chariot across the sky.

The words were scarcely spoken when Apollo regretted his oath. A mortal may, perhaps, break his word, but not so a god who had sworn by the waters of the Styx. Apollo knew that the request meant death for a mortal, and he used every argument to dissuade his son from a venture that was suicide.

"You cannot possibly keep the horses under control. I, a god, can scarcely manage them. Even Zeus himself couldn't drive the chariot. The heavens are dangerous. You will have to keep to the path, past the horns of the hostile Bull, past the Thracian Archer and the paws of the raging Lion, past the Scorpion's cruel pincers and the clutching claws of the Crab. Release me from my promise. Ask anything else and I shall grant it."

But Phaëthon, full of confidence, would not change his mind, and the reluctant Apollo had the swift Hours yoke his team, lead the four fire-breathing steeds from the stable, and fasten on the jingling harness.

No sooner had the proud youth leaped into the chariot and taken the reins in his hands than the horses knew they had not the firm hands of their master to guide them. Feeling their burden was too light, off they raced, out of control. The lad was panic-stricken. He did not know the path, he did not even know the names of the horses, and he was not able to manage the horses, even had he known. He could only cling helplessly to the sides of the swaying chariot as it plunged hither and thither through the sky.

For the first time, the cold stars of the Northern Plough grew hot, and the Serpent which lay close to the icy pole was roused to fury as it sweltered in the heat. Phaëthon's terror mounted as he sighted the Scorpion and the other monstrous beasts sprawling over the face of the high heavens. Then the horses went plunging downward towards the earth. The heat of the sun's rays seared the ground, destroying vegetation and drying up rivers and seas. Great cities perished and whole nations were reduced to ashes. So close did the chariot come to Africa that Libya became a desert and the inhabitants of Ethiopia had their skins burned to a dark hue.

Everywhere the ground gaped open and great beams of light descended even to Tartarus, frightening the king of the underworld and his queen. Three times did Poseidon try to emerge above the waters, but the fiery air was too much for him.

It was then that the alarmed Zeus had to interfere, or the whole world would have perished in flame. Mounting to the highest point of heaven, he let fly a powerful thunderbolt against the young charioteer, which dashed the luckless Phaëthon to earth.

His body fell into the Po River, and the Italian nymphs buried it on the bank. On a rock, they set this inscription:

"Here Phaëthon lies: his father's car he tried—
Though proved too weak, he greatly daring died."

ECHOES IN LITERATURE

Because of his behaviour in the myth, Phaëthon has been adopted by poets, particularly the Elizabethans, as a symbol for rashness and folly.

ECHOES IN ART

Myths treated in the preceding section were popular subjects for painting and sculpture at various times.

Greek sculptors of the fifth century B.C. and after, and the Roman sculptors who later imitated them, had a great interest in portraying idealized human beauty. The magnificent figures they chiselled were often considered portraits of the gods. Aphrodite was understandably the most popular subject, but numerous famous statues exist of almost all the other gods. Many of them, sometimes broken, are preserved and may be seen in the world's museums, notably the British Museum in London, the Louvre in Paris, and many collections in Rome.

During the early Christian era, the Greek and Roman gods and heroes fell into disrepute as Christianity supplanted paganism and introduced new moral standards. As temples were turned to other uses and the old stories were forgotten, artists devoted themselves to Biblical subjects, stories of saints and martyrs, and the glorification of God.

Not until the Renaissance did artists branch out from the religious tradition to find inspiration once more in classical subjects. Myths provided them with a tremendous source.

It would, of course, be impossible to mention all the fine and famous paintings of the gods. Only a few of those which vividly depict beings discussed in this section can be described.

The war with the Titans is vividly pictured by Rubens. His painting (Musée de Ville, Brussels) shows the mighty forms of the giants buckling under the weight of tremendous boulders hurled at them by the Hundred-Handed Ones. A famous work by Titian (Prado, Madrid) shows the punishment of Prometheus: heavy chains bind the writhing Titan to the rocks; his body twists in an effort to avoid the pain as his side is torn by the cruel talons and beak of the vulture.

A painting by Goya (Prado, Madrid) is one of the most horrifying of all those on mythological subjects. It is the Spanish master's representation of Cronus devouring his children, and shows the Titan as a grotesque ogre, stuffing the limp body of a child into his gaping mouth.

Paintings of the Olympian gods are innumerable. Probably the most famous is Botticelli's *Birth of Venus* (Uffizi gallery, Florence), which shows Aphrodite mounted upon a scallop shell, floating over the waves. Aphrodite has been painted as well with most of her loves; among these paintings is Titian's *Venus and Adonis* (National Gallery of Art, Washington).

The loves of Zeus proved a most popular subject, and inspired painters like Titian, whose greatest works include *The Abduction of Europa*, and the very famous *Danaë and the Shower of Gold* (Prado, Madrid), depicting the mother of Perseus, reclining in her dungeon, receiving Zeus in the form of a precious golden shower (see page 72).

A famous painting of *Leda and the Swan* in the Spiridon Collection, Rome, shows the woman and her huge white swan standing lovingly together, while at her feet two eggs have split open, each revealing two tiny babies—Helen, Clytemnestra, Castor and Polydeuces. This is one of the few known paintings by Leonardo da Vinci.

Several painters attempted to picture early mankind as depicted in the myths. The hunting scene painted by Piero de Cosimo (Metropolitan Museum of Art, New York) shows brutish men grappling with wild animals and fighting among themselves as well. In their company sport satyrs and centaurs.

Visions of Parnassus, the mount of the Muses, show a variety of interpretations. Mantegna, on the one hand, shows the Muses leading a frolicking dance (Louvre, Paris), while Raphael shows them listening most demurely to divine music (Vatican, Rome).

Possibly the best-known artistic representation of a god is the statue of Eros which stands in Piccadilly Circus, London. The statue is a monument to the nineteenth-century statesman, Lord Shaftesbury, who worked tirelessly to improve working conditions in industry; it symbolizes his great love for mankind.

PART TWO

MORTALS

Many of the most popular myths are stories of how the gods changed men and women into strange and different forms. Most of them are told by the Roman poet Ovid, in a book called Metamorphoses.

ARACHNE

THE most gifted of all the maidens of Lydia was Arachne. From far and near, people thronged to the city to see the wonderful tapestries the princess wove; even the gods came to stare in admiration. Word of the amazing talent of Arachne eventually reached the ears of Athene, goddess of handicrafts, who held herself to be the undisputed mistress of the loom.

So much praise and glory turned the head of the skilful maiden, until one day she actually boasted that her work was finer even than that of the goddess. Surrounded by marvelling nymphs and mortals as an intricate scene of the Olympian gods at play emerged under her nimble fingers, the headstrong girl exclaimed, "There! Let Athene do better than that!"

"I will!" shouted the angry Athene. What mortal had ever been so bold, to challenge a goddess?

So a contest was held.

When Athene examined the work of Arachne, she recognized how amazingly beautiful it really was. In a fit of jealous rage, she tore the tapestry to shreds. Terrified and ashamed, poor Arachne hanged herself from the rafters. Although she saved the girl's life, to add a final humiliation Athene turned Arachne's dangling body into that of a grotesque creature, known ever after as an arachnid, or spider.

IN HISTORY

The story of Arachne may be more than an attempt to explain the origin of the spider.

The Lydians and Carians, who are believed to be of Cretan origin, probably rivalled the Greeks in sea trade. Some of their cities were widely famed for dyed woollens, and the emblem on the seals of some of these cities is a spider. Thus, the myth may reflect the jealous rivalry in woven products which existed between these people with the spider-seal and the Greeks, represented by Athene.

PYGMALION

PYGMALION was a young sculptor whose talent rivalled even that of Hephaestus. His was the gift of carving and polishing marble into forms so beautiful, so lifelike, that the most sophisticated onlooker was bound to gasp with envy and amazement.

The young genius had an attitude strange in one so devoted to beauty. Since the time when he had fallen in love with a goddess and she had disdained him, Pygmalion had turned completely against women.

Perhaps to show the women of the world how imperfect they were, Pygmalion decided to create in marble the ideal of feminine beauty. For years he worked over the stone, gently shaping it into a flawless marvel. Never had any work of art been so successful—every detail was of a perfection that no woman, perhaps not even a goddess, could attain.

When the project was finished, Pygmalion, who could love no mortal woman, fell in love with his marble creation and became the most miserable man on earth.

Although he kissed the lovely lips of his statue, the cold marble could not respond. He clasped her hands, knelt before her, pleaded with her to love him—but all in vain. He even turned to make-believe, and waited upon her as he would have done to please a real life love; yet she remained cold and Pygmalion remained lonely. And far off on Olympus, the goddess of love laughed to see the lovesick misery of the man who had so often denounced love.

At last, Pygmalion knew he would go mad if his love for a statue continued to torment him. In desperation, he made a pilgrimage to a distant festival in honour of Aphrodite, intending to ask her where he could find a live woman who could rival his marble love.

When she saw the unhappiness in the eyes of Pygmalion, the goddess felt guilt at her own mocking of him. Her heart softened, and she made a special sign to the sculptor.

Hardly daring to hope, Pygmalion rushed home. He was disappointed when he saw that there was no lovely woman awaiting him, no one except his statue, cold and magnificent upon her pedestal. He knew then that he would never have anyone but her.

With a sigh he reached out and touched her, then leaped back in astonishment. Was it his imagination, or was the lifeless marble warm and soft? As he stared, the statue smiled at him, stepped down from her pedestal, and came into his arms.

For all their long lives Pygmalion and Galatea, the statue who had become a woman and his wife, paid daily tribute to Aphrodite, the goddess who took pity on a man who hated women.

ECHOES IN LITERATURE

The story of Pygmalion is one of today's best-known myths, largely because of two tremendously successful literary works.

Although the theme had been used a number of times in English literature, it did not really come to life until the presentation of George Bernard Shaw's play *Pygmalion*. In Shaw's modern version, Pygmalion is Henry Higgins, a woman-hating professor of phonetics who undertakes to create a perfect woman from a lowly Cockney flower-girl, by teaching her how to speak and behave like a duchess.

Two generations later, the play was turned into the musical *My Fair Lady*, by Lerner and Lowe, which in stage and screen versions proved to be among the most successful musical productions of all time.

ORPHEUS

ORPHEUS, a wandering musician of Thrace, composed the most beautiful songs the world has ever known.

While still a young man, Orpheus married a maiden known as Eurydice. Perhaps the Fates were envious of the deep, pure love of the musician and the maiden, for very soon after the wedding, as Eurydice ran through the fields, a serpent sprang from its grassy hiding place and sank its fangs into her foot. The venom coursed through her blood like fire, and she died before anyone could make a move to help her.

Even after the anguish of Orpheus' first grief had passed, he felt only emptiness and desolation where once there had been happiness. Unwilling to accept the separation, he went in search of his beloved. He went where no mortal had ever gone, through the dark cavern in the poplar grove and down, down, until finally he reached the River Styx which separates the world of the living from the dim land of the dead. As he entered the forbidden realm, he played his lyre and sang, and the thin ghosts were moved to tears by his music.

So tender was his song and so deep the love he showed that the ruler of the underworld decided to let Orpheus take his Eurydice back to the upper world. There was only one condition; to prove his faith in Hades, Orpheus must lead the way up from the underworld without so much as a glance to see if his wife were following.

Orpheus accepted the condition, for he had no choice. Nervously he began the long, slow climb back to the world of life, listening attentively for the following footsteps of Eurydice. He knew that she was still suffering from the bite of the snake, for her footsteps were uneven, as if she were limping; and though he slowed his pace, her steps fell further and further behind. Orpheus knew that if she fell and could not rise, she would be lost to him forever.

Just as the light of the sky could be seen through the cavern mouth, Orpheus could restrain himself no longer. As he turned to make sure that Eurydice was still following him, she faded away from his sight, stretching her arms out towards her husband; though he reached desperately for her, she faded back forever into the land of the dead.

With his beloved wife snatched from him a second time, Orpheus could find no peace. No longer could he call even Thrace his home, but was driven to wander over all lands. His lyre no longer played tunes to lighten the hearts of their hearers, but lonely melodies that made men bow their heads and weep. The words of Orpheus' songs remained so beautiful even in sadness that, as he passed, all living things of the earth stopped, enchanted by the music.

One day Orpheus wandered near a group of Maenads, women who worshipped their god Dionysus in frenzied rites. Instead of being calmed by the sweet song they were driven to even wilder frenzy, and in their mindlessness attacked the poet and tore him to pieces. Although the gods turned the Maenads into trees as punishment, no one could restore life to the murdered singer.

Yet Orpheus was given a strange kind of immortality. His head and the lyre he carried fell into a river and floated to the sea; still singing, they were carried by the waves to the isle of Lesbos. With them went the gift of song which made the people of Lesbos the greatest poets of the ancient world. The soul of Orpheus descended to the underworld where his beloved Eurydice awaited him, and the lovers were united at last.

IN HISTORY

The cult of Orpheus was among the most interesting of ancient religions. Regarding the poet as its centre, the religion taught such doctrines as man's divine origin, the fall of man and original sin, reincarnation, and heavenly reward for the good. Although it lasted some five centuries before being displaced by Christianity, the religion did not become widespread because it restricted its teachings to those initiated into its mysteries.

ECHOES IN LITERATURE

Composers in all the arts have found the image of Orpheus, whose poetry and song moved all who heard them, immensely appealing. One of the most famous references is that in *Henry VIII* by Shakespeare and Fletcher, that Orpheus

> . . . with his lute made trees
> And the mountain tops that freeze
> Bow themselves when he did sing.

Countless writers have borrowed some elements of the Orpheus theme in stories of separated lovers.

It is perhaps fitting that some of the most famous compositions associated with Orpheus should be musical. Among them are Gluck's opera *Orpheus and Eurydice*, which gives the ascent from the underworld a happy ending, and Offenbach's *Orpheus in the Underworld*.

THE greatest love of the goddess Aphrodite was Adonis.

Aphrodite first saw Adonis when he was just an infant, and loved him even then. Her affection lasted through Adonis' boyhood, and grew deep and intense when he matured into a clean-limbed young hunter.

When Adonis roamed the forests and hillsides in search of the stag, Aphrodite would descend from her swan-drawn carriage and, dressed like the goddess of the chase, would hunt by her lover's side. She wished to be with him always, to protect him from the forest-dwellers who, she knew, could so easily tear the life from a man—the wolf, the bear, and the fearful wild boar.

Although she had cautioned Adonis again and again against the dangerous beasts, the valiant hunter took her warnings lightly.

One day Aphrodite did not catch sight of her beloved as he set out alone to the hills. He stalked his prey without her, and forgot her words when the first beast the dogs aroused from the forest depths turned out to be the very one against which she had warned him so often, the great tusked boar.

Exhilarated by the prospect of a great trophy, Adonis let fly his spear, but failed to take careful aim. The weapon only grazed the side of the quarry. Enraged, the boar lunged through the undergrowth, and before Adonis could jump aside, the beast buried its razor-like tusk deep in his white flesh.

From far away, Aphrodite heard the dying moans of her lover. She flew to his side, but too late. Her kisses and pleading words flowed over a lifeless body from which the drops of ruby blood still dripped.

Even in her anguish, the goddess could give a kind of immortality.

"From every drop of blood shall spring a flower, and though it dies, each spring shall see it born again. The laments of every generation of maidens and youths shall echo my weeping over your death, and their rejoicing at your rebirth shall be my joy."

As she spoke, the drops of Adonis' blood turned into the anemone, the fragrant wind-flower which still blooms for a little while, then dies.

IN HISTORY

The story of Adonis is only one of a series of myths which explain the origin of trees and flowers. Another very like it is the story of Hyacinthus, beloved friend of Apollo killed by the god in an accident, whose blood turned to the hyacinth flower.

Charming as they are, such myths present a terrifying glimpse into very ancient times. Many scholars believe they recall a time of human sacrifice, when victims' blood was sprinkled on the earth as an offering to some god or spirit. When red flowers bloomed nearby, the people might seek to forget their guilt by telling that the sacrificial victim had not really died, but had just been turned into a flower. Other myths dealing with the tragic death of a handsome youth and his subsequent acceptance into some kind of immortality are generally thought to be of the same type.

The name Adonis comes from the Semitic word *Adon*, meaning *my lord*, which the Greeks mistook for a proper name. Under a variety of names, Adonis was revered through much of the ancient world, and many rituals have been identified with the celebration of his death and flower resurrection.

ECHOES IN LITERATURE

The tragic theme of Aphrodite's love for Adonis has been used over and over in literature. The most famous example in English is Shakespeare's *Venus and Adonis*, in which the goddess is shown as the pursuer, the man as the pursued. Spenser, too, used the myth (as he did a vast number of others) in the *Faerie Queene*.

One of our best-known elegies (poems in praise and mourning of the dead) is modelled upon an ancient lament for Adonis. Shelley, deeply moved by the death of fellow-poet John Keats, took his inspiration from a second-century B.C. poem by Bion, and named his mourning work *Adonais*.

IDAS, king of the Brigians, was the son of a goddess, and might have been expected to have some of the divine in his nature. Instead, he seemed to have inherited all his ways from his father, who was a satyr. As a king Midas was distinguished by only two things: his love of wine and his pursuit of wealth.

One day the old satyr Silenus, tutor of the wine-god Dionysus himself, became separated from his companions and sought refuge at the court of Midas. Since he was an amusing old fellow, the satyr was well-entertained by the king and lingered for several days at the court. Dionysus, not knowing what had happened to him, worried over his friend's absence, and when Silenus finally returned the god was almost overcome with relief. As a gesture of his thanks to Midas for looking after the satyr, he asked the king to name his reward.

The pleasure-loving king answered quickly and thoughtlessly.

"If you want to thank me, make everything I touch turn to gold," he said.

No answer was given, and Midas, to test the god's power, began to hurry through his great hall. He touched everything he could reach—furniture, ornaments, even his great throne, and to his delight, all turned to gold. Midas, in seconds, had become the richest man in the world.

Intoxicated by his success, Midas raced through the rest of the palace. All day he touched things, until not even the walls themselves failed to gleam with gold. When nothing was left, the elated Midas called for a royal feast to be spread before him to celebrate the day's good fortune.

Hungrily he raised the first morsel to his lips—but jumped when he tried to bite into it. It was gold! He tried another, and another—but not a crust, not a crumb could he swallow. As long as he merely looked at the food, it remained tempting and savoury, but as soon as his fingers or lips touched it, it became cold, hard gold. Horrified, Midas pushed the platter away and reached for his goblet, to quench his thirst; but the water in the cup turned to liquid gold as soon as it touched the king's lips.

For several days Midas grew steadily more and more hungry. When at last he could stand no more, he threw himself prostrate upon the ground.

"Great god Dionysus," he moaned, "if there is any mercy in your soul, take back this curse with which you have afflicted me!"

"Bathe in the waters of the river," the king was told. Midas bathed, and when he emerged from the running stream, he saw the river sands glittering with gold dust. The terrible blessing he had asked of the god was gone.

Years later, Midas again became foolishly involved with the gods. He was asked to help judge a musical contest, and loudly announced that he disagreed with the opinion expressed by the other judges, who were Olympian deities. When he arrived at his home, he discovered to his astonished horror that growing from his head was a pair of ass's ears—the gods' frank way of announcing their opinion of his musical appreciation.

Midas tried to hide his embarrassment under a hat, and the only man who had to know of the affliction, his barber, was sworn to secrecy. But as time went on, the barber simply could not keep the secret any longer. He had to tell somebody or he felt he would burst; so he went to the river bank, dug a deep hole, and shouted into it, "King Midas has ass's ears!"

He never told anyone else, but a reed who grew from the river bank whispered the king's terrible secret to all who passed by. It was not long before all the world knew that from the head of the king grew the ears of an ass, and laughed at the foolish king for the rest of his life.

ECHO AND NARCISSUS

OT many men, or even gods, were as handsome as young Narcissus. So fair was he that almost everyone who saw him fell in love with him that very moment.

One day, as Narcissus roamed the forests with his hunting companions, he was spied by the watchful eye of the nymph Echo. She had once been a great chatterer, ready to talk to any passerby on any subject at any time, and on several occasions she had detained the goddess Hera with hours of casual talk, just as Hera was on the point of stumbling upon Zeus with one of his illicit loves. Eventually Hera grew so annoyed that she put a curse on Echo, and from that time on the unfortunate nymph could say nothing but the last few words that she had heard.

Trembling, Echo followed Narcissus through the trees. She longed to go closer to him, to gaze upon the beauty of his face, but she feared that he would laugh at her silly speech. Before long Narcissus wandered away from his companions, and when he realized he was lost, he called in panic, "Is there anybody here?"

"Here!" called Echo.

Mystified by this reply, Narcissus shouted, "Come!"

"Come!" shouted Echo.

Narcissus was convinced that someone was playing tricks on him.

"Why are you avoiding me?" he called. The only answer he heard was his own question repeated from the woods.

"Come here, and let us meet!" pleaded Narcissus.

"Let us meet!" Echo answered, delighted.

She overcame her shyness, and crept from her hiding place to approach Narcissus. But he, satisfied now that he had solved the mystery of the voice, roughly pushed her away and ran.

"I would die before I would have you near me!" he shouted mockingly over his shoulder.

Helpless, Echo had to call after him, "I would have you near me!"

The nymph was so embarrassed and ashamed that she hid herself in a dark cave, and never came into the air and sunlight again. Her youth and beauty withered away, and her body became so shrunken and tiny that eventually she vanished altogether. All that was left was the pathetic voice which still roams the world, anxious to talk, yet able only to repeat what others say.

Poor Echo was not the only one to be treated brutally by Narcissus. He had played with many hearts, and at last one of those he had scorned prayed to the gods that Narcissus would some day find himself scorned by one he loved. The prayer was heard, and granted.

Tired and thirsty from his hunting, Narcissus threw himself down beside a still, clear pool to drink. As he leaned over the shining surface, he saw reflected the most beautiful face he had ever seen. His heart trembled at the sight, and he could not tear himself away from it—his own image.

For a long time Narcissus remained there beside the pool, never raising his eyes from the surface, and from time to time murmuring words of love. At last his body withered away and became the stem of a flower, and his head the lovely gold and white blossom which still looks into quiet pools, and is called the narcissus.

HERO AND LEANDER

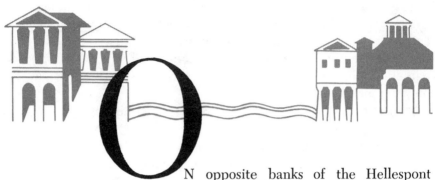

O N opposite banks of the Hellespont stood the towns of Sestos and Abydos. In the town of Sestos lived a priestess of Aphrodite, named Hero; she was adored by a young man of Abydos, Leander.

Every night Leander plunged into the Hellespont and swam its treacherous width to visit his love, and every night Hero lit a torch on top of a lighthouse, to guide her lover across.

One terrible night the sky grew black with thunder-clouds, the wind blew, and torrential rain drowned Hero's torch. Leander was engulfed in the blackness of night and lost his way.

The next morning, the lover's wave-battered body was washed up on the shore where he was accustomed to meet Hero. She knew that he had died trying to reach her and, unable to live without him, Hero took her own life.

ECHOES IN LITERATURE

Several of England's greatest poets have found inspiration in the story of Hero and Leander. Probably the most successful treatment of the theme is Christopher Marlowe's long poem entitled *Hero and Leander*. From this work comes one of the best-known lines in our language:

Who ever lov'd, that lov'd not at first sight?

Other famous references to the story were made by Byron, Rossetti, Tennyson and Keats.

PSYCHE

I T was rare indeed to find a mortal who could arouse the envy of one of the inhabitants of Olympus, but such was the case with Psyche.

This maiden was so beautiful in face and form that she caused jealousy to enter the heart of great Aphrodite, the love goddess who was certainly among the most beautiful in heaven. Mortal men, too, considered Psyche the loveliest thing they had ever laid eyes upon, and sometimes even forgot their worship of Aphrodite in their rapture over Psyche. But strangely, although all admired her, no one actually came close to her, to know her gentle nature and fall in love with her.

Once, when she had overheard some men praising Psyche's beauty more than her own, Aphrodite jealously called Eros to her.

"Go and touch the heart of that vile woman," she said. "Make her fall in love with some horrible monster . . ." for after being struck by one of Eros' shafts, a person fell in love with the first thing he saw.

But Aphrodite had foolishly underestimated the beauty of Psyche, for no sooner did Eros see her than he himself was smitten by an overwhelming passion for her and could not bear to carry out his mother's order.

Despite her beauty, Psyche remained alone, unloved, until finally her father began to worry that he would have a spinster to look after. He consulted the oracles for a solution.

"You must take Psyche and leave her on the mountain-top," the oracle said, "and there she must wait for her destined husband, a fearsome dragon."

Heavy-hearted, the father of Psyche obeyed.

Poor Psyche, left solitary on the lonely mountain, sure that she would never see her family again, fearful that she was to be eaten by some dread creature, cried herself to sleep . . . She awoke beside a shining palace whose doors seemed to beckon to her. When she entered, there was no one to be seen, but voices spoke to her out of the air.

"This is your home, and we are your servants," the voices said. "Live here in comfort and happiness, for this is the palace you will share with your husband."

When night fell, Psyche's husband came to her, and she fell in love with his kind voice and gentle ways, although she was not allowed to see him.

"You must never try to look at me," his voice told her, "for if you do, I must leave you forever."

Psyche obeyed him, and their life together became an idyll.

Much later, Psyche's two sisters came to seek her. They were surprised to find her alive, and amazed by the wonderful palace in which she lived—so amazed that their hearts grew envious.

"Poor little sister," they said deceitfully. "How terrible it must be to be married to a monster whom you have never seen and who one night will surely devour you. How we pity you!"

When they had gone, Psyche was tormented by doubts and questions. She loved her gentle husband, yet who was he? Was he so horrible that he had always to hide from her?

That night, when her husband had fallen asleep, Psyche could stand the strain no longer. Taking a lamp, she cautiously lit it and held it over her husband's sleeping form. In her other hand she held a knife in case he should actually prove to be a vicious monster.

But there before her lay the most wonderful being she had ever seen; indeed, more wonderful than any other, for it was the god of love himself.

Psyche was so thrilled and startled that she leaned over her husband to study his features more carefully, and as she did so, a few drops of oil tipped from the lamp and scalded his shoulder. Eros awoke.

"How could you do this?" he cried. "Love cannot live without trust!" —and he faded away from her.

Psyche realized the terrible thing she had done, and cried for her love to return, but no one came.

She appealed to the gods of Olympus to help her, but all knew of Aphrodite's enmity towards her, and no one dared offend the goddess of love.

Finally, she appealed to Aphrodite herself.

The great goddess' pride was soothed to have the most beautiful mortal of all time come pleading to her. Scornfully, she told her that she must carry out many tasks, for such a plain girl must prove her worth before the goddess of love would help her find a husband!

The first task she set Psyche was to separate a great pile of varied grain into its separate kinds. Impossible though the task seemed, it was accomplished within the time allotted. The little ants, sensing Psyche's desperation, did it for her.

The second task was to fetch golden fleece from fierce sheep; the reeds by the river where they drank caught the wool for her.

Next, the goddess ordered Psyche to fetch a jar of water from the source of the River Styx. As she stood by the dreaded spring, despairing, an eagle snatched the jar, bore it to the stream, and returned with it filled.

In a final effort to terrify the girl, Aphrodite sent her to the underworld to fetch some beauty from Persephone. Even this Psyche accomplished, so great was her love. She was stopped temporarily by Cerberus, but won him by feeding him bits of cake.

Finally, Eros himself intervened. Psyche had proved herself, and had lived down her terrible mistrust. Appealing to Zeus, he persuaded the king of the gods to elevate Psyche to a goddess, and to allow her to live on Olympus as his wife.

DAEDALUS AND ICARUS

constant trouble-maker in ancient Athens was the craftsman Daedalus. Though his talent raised him far above the ranks of the ordinary citizens—indeed, he had been taught metal-work by Athene herself—he was jealous of anyone whom he suspected might some day rival him.

He had taken as his apprentice his nephew, Talus, and taught him so well that there came a time when Talus seemed to challenge his uncle's reputation as the master-craftsman of Athens. Daedalus was unable to control his jealousy. Forgetting in his rage the loyalty the young man had shown him, forgetting even that he was his own kins-man, Daedalus lured Talus to the highest point of the city walls, and pushed him over the edge.

Murder of a kinsman was considered the most heinous crime of all, and Daedalus fled across the sea where no one would know of his crime. His pride prevented him, however, from concealing his identity, and he found that although his crime was unknown in Crete, his repu-tation as a brilliant craftsman was well-established. Minos himself, king of Crete, received him with delight, for he had been looking for some outstanding craftsman to build a huge maze to house the Minotaur.

This monster, half bull and half man, devoured a tribute of seven Athenian youths and seven maidens every nine years. The oppressed Athenians finally gained release from the tribute through the heroism of Theseus, who entered the maze, or labyrinth, killed the Minotaur, then found his way out again. When Minos heard of the incredible deed, he blamed Daedalus, for he was convinced that no one could have found his way through the labyrinth's complex of tunnels without the assistance of its designer. The king's anger grew, until the life of Daedalus was in grave danger.

Although all escape routes from Crete were closed to him, Daedalus' craftmanship proved stronger than the king's power. He built two pairs of wings, one for himself and one for his son Icarus, bigger and stronger than the wings of any bird. They were made of feathers which in some places were sewn together, and in others, joined by wax. With the wonderful inventions securely strapped to their bodies, Daedalus and Icarus prepared to take to the air.

Before they flew off, Daedalus had one warning for his son, for he well knew Icarus' foolhardy nature.

"Be sure to follow me closely, my son," he cautioned. "We must not stray from our course, for it will be easy to get lost. Above all, we must not fly too high. Do not mount above me, but stay on the level where I fly."

Icarus nodded in understanding, and father and son leaped into the air and soared away from Crete.

For a time all was well. Then Daedalus looked over his shoulder for his son, and found no Icarus following. Desperately he scanned the skies, and perceived, far above him, a tiny speck moving further and further away, climbing higher and higher. Daedalus knew that Icarus had forgotten his warning, and had become intoxicated by the sensation of flying, but he was helpless. Unable to save his son, Daedalus could only watch while Icarus climbed and climbed, until at last the sun melted the wax of his wings, and he plummetted into the sea. The place where he drowned has become known, after him, as the Icarian Sea.

ECHOES IN LITERATURE

The modern novelist James Joyce gave the aspiring artist who is the hero of his *Portrait of the Artist as a Young Man* the name of Stephen Dedalus.

Icarus has become a more popular literary symbol than his father. Sometimes he symbolizes reckless bravery, sometimes dreams that are doomed to be dashed to earth.

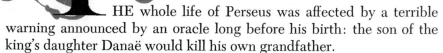

HE whole life of Perseus was affected by a terrible warning announced by an oracle long before his birth: the son of the king's daughter Danaë would kill his own grandfather.

When Danaë's father Acrisius heard this frightful warning, he resolved that his daughter would never bear any children. She was never to be allowed to marry, he decided; and he built a special bronze dungeon sunk deep into the ground, completely closed off from the world except for a small grilled opening to admit light and air. In this impenetrable palace he imprisoned his daughter.

In spite of all such precautions, the lovely Danaë did bear a child, for one day Zeus himself came to her as a shower of golden sunlight which poured down through the tiny window. She kept the child, a boy whom she named Perseus, hidden for as long as she could, for she knew how terrible her father's anger could be. When Acrisius inevitably discovered the child, he was, as she had expected, furious.

Acrisius faced the dilemma of getting rid of his ordained murderer without summoning the wrath of the gods upon his own head. The killing of a kinsman was one of the few deeds which horrified the gods, and they inflicted terrible punishments on anyone who committed such a crime. However, thought Acrisius craftily, they could do nothing to him if he merely placed a kinsman in the way of probable death.

The old king sealed his daughter and her son up in a chest without food or water, bolted the locks tightly, and dropped the chest into the sea. As it floated out of sight, he heaved a great sigh of relief.

But by good fortune or the aid of Zeus, a great wave swept the chest to a small island, where it was discovered by a fisherman. He looked curiously at it, and was about to abandon it as but another of the strange objects washed in by the ocean when he heard a muffled banging from within. Immediately he knocked it apart with sharp rocks from the beach, and rushed the two hungry, bedraggled refugees to his home.

Perseus grew up to be a helper of his fisherman foster-father, and his mother Danaë led a peaceful, contented life on the island. Worry-free years made her even lovelier than she had been as a girl—so lovely that eventually the eye of the island's ruler fell upon her.

Although the king was enchanted by Danaë, he hated and resented her son, now grown to manhood; all the time he was courting the mother, he was seeking a plan which would remove Perseus from her company once and for all.

The opportunity arose when Perseus, raised as a poor fisherman, was unable to offer any wedding gift to the king and his mother. By playing on the young man's embarrassment, the king won from him a promise to bring as a wedding offering the head of Medusa, the Gorgon.

Perseus was overwhelmed by the immensity of the task. The Gorgons were three monster-sisters whose heads were entwined with writhing, venomous snakes instead of hair, and whose faces were so incredibly ugly that whoever so much as glanced at them would be turned to stone. Although Medusa was the only mortal among the sisters, she was really as well protected as the others, for it seemed impossible to find and kill her without seeing her face. Moreover, there was a good chance that he would never be able even to attempt the kill, for no one was able to tell him exactly where Medusa and the Gorgons could be found.

Wise men, oracles, travellers—all were consulted by Perseus when he reached the mainland of Greece, but all in vain. No one could answer his questions. For months he wandered over the hills of Greece, always hoping that some person, somehow, would be able to help him; always, he was disappointed.

This son of Zeus, however, was favoured by the gods. Just when he was at his most disconsolate, when his quest seemed absolutely futile, a radiant being suddenly appeared before him. He wore a winged hat and winged sandals, and even his golden staff bore wings. Perseus knew that he was face to face with Hermes, the messenger of the gods. He fell on his knees, shaken that he should be so honoured; and when he raised his eyes, he saw that not one but two radiant beings stood before him. The goddess Athene, too, had befriended Perseus, and together the two deities offered the youth the solutions to his problems.

First, announced Hermes, Perseus needed special equipment. He could give him a sword which the scales of Medusa could not blunt or break. Athene could give the polished shield she wore on her own breast, and by looking into its mirror-bright surface, Perseus could avoid looking directly at the Gorgons and so save himself from being turned to stone.

The other things were not so easy to obtain. To get them, Perseus would have to visit the nymphs of the North, the Hyperboreans who lived at the back of the North Wind; the only persons who could tell him where to find the nymphs were the Graiae, the Gray-haired Women who dwelt in the land of twilight.

Perseus learned from Hermes the trick he would have to play to force the Graiae to give him the directions he needed. The three women had among them only one eye, which they used in turn. Each wore it to see for a few minutes, then plucked it from its place in her forehead and passed it to one of her sisters. Perseus was to watch for the moment when the eye was being passed and all three sisters were blind, and at the crucial second was to snatch away the precious eye and use it as a bargaining device.

He carried out this distasteful adventure successfully, and soon was bound for the country of the Hyperboreans.

The nymphs proved to be friendly; they welcomed the stranger with feasts and dancing, and presented him with three gifts to be used for the fight against Medusa: winged sandals which would carry him through the air as swiftly as Hermes, a helmet which made its wearer invisible, and a magic bag which could adjust its size to fit whatever was to be carried in it. Armed with the gifts and at last learning directions to the Gorgons' land, Perseus finally set out to do the deed he had promised.

He approached the rocky island where the Gorgons lived with hesitation and fear, for all his instincts told him to flee. But he had been instructed well, and held all his magic weapons in readiness. Fortune was on his side, for as he swept low over the island, he discerned the huddled forms of the ghastly sisters—asleep. For a moment he was disconcerted by the discovery that he did not know which of the three was the mortal Medusa, but Hermes and Athena appeared, out of thin air, and quickly pointed her out to him.

Carefully keeping his eyes fixed upon the shield, Perseus swooped down to the sleeping forms and with one great sweep of his magic sword, lopped off Medusa's head.

Without looking at it, he dropped it into the bag which had magically expanded to hold the head and its still-twisting serpents. Then he raced away, thankful for the special cap which made him invisible, for the other Gorgons, awakened by the agonized death-scream of their sister, pursued him into the night.

Perseus set off for home, pausing on the way only long enough to rescue from a monster a lovely maiden, Andromeda, and to claim her for his wife.

Upon his arrival at the island, things were not at all as he had known them. Perseus could find neither his mother nor the friendly fisherman, and he soon learned that when Danaë had finally refused to wed the king, she had been forced to flee from his wrath. Her faithful protector had followed her.

Furious at the deadly mission on which the king had knowingly sent him, and enraged at the treatment of his mother, Perseus knew what he must do. He strode off towards the king's palace.

Every eye in the great hall turned to the young man as he made his dramatic entrance. The king, sure that Perseus had been killed long before, stared speechless. Before anyone could recover his senses, Perseus snatched into the bag and held the head of Medusa aloft. Everyone looked—and then all was still in the great hall, and Perseus walked away from the stone figures which had a moment before been a king and his courtiers.

Later, after he found his mother, Perseus decided to go with her to Greece, to meet his grandfather and reconcile the family. He was invited in his home city to take part in an athletic contest, and as he threw the discus, it was strangely deflected and struck the old king Acrisius. Perseus had not escaped his destiny, after all.

HE magnificent appearance and winning personality of the young man Bellerophon caused many citizens of his native Corinth to suspect that his father was the god Poseidon himself. Though of course nothing could be proven, the idea that perhaps he was of immortal descent pleased Bellerophon, and he longed to do deeds worthy of his parentage.

However, he first became famous for a deed which caused men not to sing his praises, but to shudder in horror. Bellerophon killed his brother—by accident, some conceded; still, fratricide was a deed repugnant to gods and man, and the person who committed it would have to go far from his home and somehow find purification.

Heartsick, Bellerophon wandered to Argos, where he was accepted into the court of the king. Although he received the purification he sought, fate still was turned against him, for the wife of the king fell in love with the young stranger. Since Bellerophon was an honourable guest, he paid no attention whatever to the queen, and his rejection so angered her that she told her husband that the visitor had wronged her and must be killed.

Well aware that the killing of a guest broke a sacred bond that the gods had instituted between guest and host, the king sent Bellerophon to visit another friend, bearing a sealed letter which contained a request that the young man be put to death.

But by the time the letter was read, that man too had accepted Bellerophon into his home and offered him hospitality. To carry out the request of his friend and yet keep from offending the gods, he hit upon a seemingly impossible task, one which would surely, he felt, bring about the young man's death: Bellerophon was to fight and slay the Chimaera.

The Chimaera was one of the most fearsome monsters of the world—a dreadful combination of serpent, goat, and lion, whose breath was pure fire. She lived on a remote mountain which Bellerophon would have to climb before even hoping to find her.

Deadly as the task seemed, Bellerophon could not refuse. Before his host he displayed nothing but eagerness; in his heart, he felt nothing but despair.

Finally a plan came to him, a plan so difficult it seemed almost as impossible as killing the Chimaera. If Bellerophon had as a special weapon the marvellous winged horse which had been born from the blood of Medusa, the Gorgon, might he not be able to conquer the Chimaera?

He would never have been able to capture the horse Pegasus had it not been for the intervention of Athene. For some reason, she took pity on the young man's plight, and gave him the means to catch the horse—a golden bridle, at the sight of which Pegasus stood tame as a packhorse.

As soon as Bellerophon mounted the back of the magic steed, Pegasus soared above the clouds, bearing him straight to the mountains where the Chimaera lived. The flying horse made the conquest easy, for Bellerophon teased the monster with arrows from a safe distance until she was distracted; then he tossed between her gaping jaws a great lump of iron. The monster's fiery breath melted the metal and it poured, red hot, down her throat. With her vital organs seared, she collapsed; Bellerophon had done the impossible.

Beginning to believe that he must indeed be the son of the god Poseidon, Bellerophon decided to take what he believed was his rightful place among the gods. Astride Pegasus, he tried to go where no earth-dweller had ever gone—to Mount Olympus.

Pegasus was wiser than his rider, and shied away from carrying him to the abode of the gods. He grew frightened and reared and plunged, and Bellerophon fell from his back. The long fall to earth did not kill him but crippled him badly, and, detested by the gods for his presumption, he roamed the earth, sick and lonely, until his death.

Pegasus continued by himself to Olympus, where he found shelter in the heavenly stables. As he became the most favoured of the beasts of the gods, he was given the privilege of carrying the thunderbolts of Zeus.

OST terrible of all the evils that ever beset the city of Athens was the tribute to the Minotaur.

Although he was called Minotaur, which means bull of Minos, the monster was actually half-human. His mother, the queen of Crete, had borne him to Poseidon's magic white bull, and he was a grotesque combination of the two forms. So ugly was his nature that King Minos kept him hidden far from human eyes in a tremendous tortuous maze, the labyrinth, which he had had commissioned to be built by the master architect Daedalus. The loneliness of his life merely increased the beast's savagery, so that no one was safe to venture inside the labyrinth at all; since he had devoured some early unfortunate adventurers, the Minotaur had grown very fond of human flesh.

Once every nine years, his greed was satisfied by the sacrifice of seven youths and seven maidens from Athens. The Athenians were forced to select the most beautiful of their youth, and every ninth year the streets of the city were filled with the wailing of mothers for the children who were to be taken over the sea and sacrificed to the Cretan monster.

So powerful was Crete that the Athenians could find no way to escape the dreadful tribute, until the king's son Theseus became filled with determination to end the bloody payments forever.

Paying no heed to the pleadings of his father, King Aegeus, Theseus insisted upon taking the place of one of the young men chosen for the sacrifice. He would, he claimed, find some way not only to save himself and rescue the other Athenian youths, but to kill the Minotaur and end its curse.

Though he mourned what he believed to be the inevitable death of his dearly-loved son, old Aegeus dared not forbid him to go; he loved the people of his city too, and wept with them when their sons and daughters were taken from them. How could he interfere in what might be their only chance for reprieve?

"I will pray to Athene for your safety, my son," he said, "and since I have always served her faithfully and done her honour, perhaps she will not toss aside an old man's prayer.

"Take this white sail, and if you live, put it up to replace the black one our tribute ship always carries. That way I and my people shall know of your success as soon as you sail over the horizon, and we may welcome you as a hero."

The sad little band of Athenians did not take long to reach the harbour of the Cretan capital, Cnossos. There, by the side of the water, waited Minos, sneering triumphantly at the fourteen timid captives who soon would be food for the Minotaur. Immediately Theseus challenged the king's prerogative to do as he wished with the captives.

His stratagem for catching the king's attention was successful.

"What, will you make fun of me?" demanded Minos. "Will you scorn the fate which we have prepared for you? Very well, then—you shall be the first to be fed to the Minotaur, and the others shall remain outside until you have faced him alone and become a mass of bloody bones!"

But there was another who noticed Theseus, who admired his boldness and manliness, and who shuddered to hear the words of the king. This was the princess Ariadne, and her soft heart ached when she thought of what would happen to the handsome lad who was brave enough to laugh at her father.

That night, a lithe form slipped past the guards into the room where Theseus was spending his last night on earth.

"I have a plan which can save you," Ariadne whispered. "This magic ball of twine was given me by Daedalus, and it knows the secrets of the labyrinth. Tie one end to the entrance, and let the ball roll on the floor. It will lead you straight to the Minotaur. When you have finished your task, wind the ball up again to find your way back to the entrance."

Theseus was filled with amazement and gratitude. He knew well that part of his problem would have been the labyrinth itself, for its corridors wound for miles, most of them leading nowhere. A man could die of starvation before he found his way out of the maze.

"And here is a sword," Ariadne continued. "Your fists would be no defence against the Minotaur, but with this sword, you may be able to stay alive. Goodbye, and may the gods watch over you!"

Next morning, Theseus began his long walk through the complexity of passages which made up the labyrinth. After what seemed hundreds of miles, he discovered the fearsome monster in the dim gloom of the inner chamber. Perhaps Athene and the gods really were on his side, for the Minotaur was asleep! Summoning all his strength, Theseus plunged Ariadne's sword into the monster's heart. With a great bellow he stumbled to his feet, eyes red with rage and jaws slavering with hunger; yet the blood poured from his breast, and in just a few seconds, with a scream he collapsed and lay still.

Then Theseus, rolling up the ball of twine as he walked, wound his way out of the labyrinth. As he emerged into the sunlight at the maze's mouth, the Cretan crowd fell silent, as if they knew that their days of sacrifice were over. Even the king's guards made no move to hinder Theseus as he went to the prison, freed his companions, and boarded the ship for home. With him he took Ariadne, but he soon forgot the debt he owed her, and abandoned her before reaching Athens.

The victorious return was marred by tragedy, for so elated was the hero that he forgot his father's request to change the black sails for white.

Aegeus had spent all the days since his son's departure pacing upon the cliffs near the city, watching for the ship which would bring glorious or tragic tidings. As he saw the black sail rise over the horizon and move slowly towards the city, the king was overcome with grief and guilt. He plunged over the cliff, and his body was smashed to pieces on the rocks below.

In honour of his father, the anguished Theseus decreed that the sea on whose shores he had died should be called after him. Filled with sorrow, Theseus took his rightful place as the new hero-king of Athens.

IN HISTORY

The story of Theseus is bound up in the legends which surround Crete, one of the most fascinating and still mysterious countries of antiquity.

Until this century, most of our knowledge of the island came from myths. We now know that Cretan civilization greatly influenced mainland Greece, so it is natural that stories of Crete, or stories that originated there, should have been woven into Greek mythology. The peculiarity which strikes the reader of these myths is the fact that a bull features prominently in all, from the story of Europa, who was borne to the island on the back of a white bull, to Theseus, who killed the bull-like monster.

Sir Arthur Evans, who conducted excavations in Crete from 1900, dug up one of the most exciting finds in archaeological history—the palace of Cnossos, so vast that it staggers the imagination. Suddenly the elements of the Theseus story became clear, for the ground plan of the palace was a tremendous maze, and everywhere appeared symbols apparently sacred to a great Cretan deity—the horns of a bull, and a two-headed ax called a **labrys**. This palace network was undoubtedly the labyrinth of the story, its name taken from the labrys symbol which everywhere decorated it. The bull, too, undoubtedly meant "Crete" to the Greeks.

We do not know whether the Cretans actually offered human sacrifices, but the story of the Athenian tribute makes such a conclusion quite possible. The story of Talus in the adventures of the Argonauts appears to be another version of a horrible fate awaiting Greeks who roamed to the island of Crete. In that story, Talus was a bronze giant who crushed aliens to death; some scholars have combined the Minotaur and Talus stories to conclude that humans were sacrificed into a huge bronze vessel, which bore the emblem of.the bull.

The actual early history of the island still has many gaps which must be filled by the imagination. Archaeologists have discovered that a civilization was growing there as early as 3000 B.C., and reached a period of greatness about 2100. A great catastrophe of some kind occurred about four centuries later, but upon the ruins was built an even greater culture.

About 1400 B.C., Cretan civilization fell. Although the Cretans themselves claimed it was a natural disaster which wrecked their civilizations, Athenians related that when Minos (which may have been a title designating the ruler, like *Pharaoh* in Egypt) set out with his navy in pursuit of Theseus, his land was left open to attack. Other tales say that during his pursuit of Daedalus, the civilization fell. Some scholars have deduced, from the mixture of myth and archaeological evidence, that a weakening Crete was finally defeated by raiders from mainland Greece. At any rate, Crete ceased about that time to be a decisive force in the history of the Mediterranean lands.

ECHOES IN LITERATURE

Although Theseus is a popular figure in literature, writers have usually chosen other events of his life to elaborate upon, rather than the slaying of the Minotaur.

One of Theseus' wives was Phaedra, who fell in love with Hippolytus, her husband's son by a previous marriage. Their tragic story ended with the death of Hippolytus in a chariot accident, and of Phaedra by her own hand. Writers like the French playwright Racine have used the lovers to create powerful tragic drama.

Theseus as the king of Athens is one of the chief characters in Shakespeare's *A Midsummer Night's Dream*, and the plot of the play centres around his marriage to Hippolyta, queen of the Amazons.

The story of Theseus found its way to the best-seller lists in recent years with the publication of two novels by Mary Renault. *The King Must Die* tells of the youthful Theseus, and a sequel, *The Bull from the Sea*, picks up his story later.

The story of Ariadne's desertion by Theseus has also been a favourite theme.

HERACLES

REATEST of all the heroes of the ancient world was Heracles, whose strength was greater than the strength of a hundred men, and who was the son of Zeus himself.

When Zeus decided to create a son who would become the world's greatest hero, for the mother he chose the mortal woman who exceeded all others in beauty, grace, and virtue: Alcmene, wife of Amphitryon. Zeus well knew that because of her strong virtue, Alcmene would have nothing to do with any man but her husband. Accordingly, he waited patiently until Amphitryon was away from home, then disguised himself as the absent husband.

Hera was so enraged at Zeus' infidelity that she tried her best to prevent Heracles from being born. She forced the goddess of birth, who was always present when a baby was being born, to sit with legs and fingers crossed outside the door of Alcmene's chamber, for while she stayed in that position, Alcmene could not give birth. At length, however, one of Alcmene's friends played a clever trick: she rushed from the birth-chamber, shouting that a fine son had been born. The birth-goddess leaped to her feet in surprise, and at that moment, off-guard, let Alcmene give birth to Heracles and his twin brother, Iphicles, who was the true son of Amphitryon.

Alcmene was terrified that Hera would try to punish her for unknowingly bearing a child of Zeus, and she tried to appease the queen of the gods by leaving the child outside the city to die of exposure. Zeus, however, found an ally in Athene, who conspired with him to make his son immortal.

Athene invited Hera to go for a walk, and led her to the place where the infant Heracles lay.

"Look!" she exclaimed in feigned surprise. "Who could have abandoned such a handsome infant? We must look after him, or he will surely die!"

Hera agreed, her heart moved by the sight of the helpless infant. Quickly she picked him up, cuddled him and, alarmed by his hungry cries, began to nurse him. As soon as she did this, Heracles became immortal.

Ignoring Hera's rage at the trick, Athene took the child and returned him to Alcmene.

"Look after him well," she said, "for he will grow up to be the greatest man the world has ever known."

The twice-tricked Hera became an implacable enemy of Heracles, and sent him troubles and difficulties throughout his life.

Hera's first attempt to destroy Heracles occurred less than a year later, one evening after Alcmene had put her twins to bed.

When all the household was asleep, Hera sent two serpents, huge, flame-eyed, and poison-fanged, to devour the son of Zeus. They coiled their way around the door of the room where the twins lay sleeping, and Iphicles, who had only been dozing, awakened to see their terrifying forms almost upon him. The child's screams as he tried to crawl away from the reptiles awakened his parents and brought them running from the next chamber.

A strange scene met their eyes. There was Iphicles, moaning in terror; there was Heracles; and there were the serpents—dead, and hanging from the hands of little Heracles, who, having picked them up to play with, had choked them to death.

When he had grown to manhood, married, and had six sons, Heracles fell once more a victim to Hera's wrath. She sent a fit of madness upon him, so that he mistook his children for enemies and killed them all. When his sanity returned, he was horrified by what he had done, and shut himself away from all company for a long time. Finally he went to the Oracle of Delphi, to beg a penance for his crime.

The Oracle sent him to one King Eurystheus, who was a favourite of Hera, and told him that Eurystheus would assign a penance.

Heracles did as he was told, and Eurystheus gave him twelve almost-impossible tasks to perform. These have since been known as the Labours of Heracles.

The first four labours which Heracles had to perform were concerned with strange beasts which roamed the ancient world.

His first task was to kill and flay the lion that lived in the vale of Nemea. No ordinary lion would have been a match for the great strength and cunning of Heracles, but the Nemean Lion was invulnerable; no weapon could penetrate its flesh. Unaware, Heracles attacked it first with his sword, which bent as though it were made of grass. Next he smote the lion a mighty blow with the club which he always carried, but the beast merely shook its head and strolled into its cave. Realizing at last the lion's magic, Heracles attacked it with his bare hands, and after a long wrestling match, choked the beast to death.

Part of his assignment had been to flay the beast, and this caused the hero some difficulty, for no knife could penetrate the animal's skin. Eventually, though, he hit upon the scheme of using the lion's own sharp claws. Ever after Heracles wore the skin as a symbol of his prowess.

The second creature which Heracles was ordered to kill proved even more difficult; it was the Hydra of Lerna, a tremendous serpent with numberless heads. One of these heads was immortal, and could not be killed. The others all had the power of growing again, multiplied by two or three, as soon as they were cut off.

Heracles took his nephew with him to help slay the Hydra, but at first they could make no progress. As soon as the hero crushed or cut off one head, several more would spring up in its place. Hera, his old enemy, was alert, for she sent a crab to the scene to aid the Hydra by biting Heracles' foot, a deed which won the crab a place among the stars as one of the signs of the Zodiac.

After hours of fruitless battle, Heracles discovered the plan which was to bring him victory. As he cut off each head, he cauterized the open wound with flame before the new heads could grow. At last even the immortal head was cut off and buried, alive and hissing, under a pile of heavy rocks.

The third labour sounded easier. There roamed on the Ceryneian Hill a beautiful, bronze-hoofed hind, sacred to Artemis. Heracles was ordered to capture this deer without spilling so much as one drop of her blood, and bring her to Eurystheus.

For a full year he pursued her, until she dropped with exhaustion. Heracles pinned her forelegs together with an arrow, which was driven so carefully that it merely punctured the skin and drew no blood, and he carried her back to the king.

Another creature whom Heracles had to capture alive was a huge wild boar which lived on Mount Erymanthus. Boars had often killed humans, Heracles knew, so he kept well out of the animal's way, tormenting it from a distance with his arrows until he drove the beast into a snow drift. While it was caught there, he bound it with chains and carried it in triumph to Eurystheus.

The wealthiest cattle-owner in the world was King Augeias of Elis. Since his cattle always gave birth to healthy young and were immune to disease, he never had bothered to have their stable cleaned. Clearing away the filth of many years was the fifth labour assigned to Heracles, and Eurystheus was almost sure that Heracles would not be able to do it because of the overwhelming smell.

However, Heracles cleaned the stables in one day, and the surrounding pastures too, without even coming near. He simply diverted the courses of two neighbouring rivers so that they rushed through the filthy farm, carrying away all dirt.

Three more labours concerning wild beasts were assigned. One was to dispose of a flock of birds in the Stymphalian Marsh, who had long, straight bronze beaks, sharp enough to cut through a man's armour, sharp bronze claws to tear up prey, and a taste for human flesh. Heracles found he could not even get near the birds, because the marsh was too watery to bear his weight. To help him, Athene gave him a pair of castanets to rattle, and their noise so frightened the birds that they flew up and circled in wild confusion. Heracles was easily able to shoot them with his arrows as they wheeled above his head.

The capture of the wild bull of Crete was next, and Heracles conquered it by wrestling, just as he had defeated the Nemean Lion.

For the eighth labour, he was ordered to bring Eurystheus the mares of King Diomedes. These mares were savage beasts, which were fed human flesh by Diomedes. Heracles first satisfied their appetite by offering them the still-living body of their master, and when they were no longer hungry, they allowed the hero to lead them away.

One of the most interesting tribes of the ancient world was the tribe of the Amazons, women who believed that the female was superior to the male, and therefore permitted men to perform only menial tasks.

They broke the arms and legs of male children so that they would be fit for nothing but household duties, and trained their daughters to be strong, disciplined warriors. They once even captured the great city of Troy, without the aid of a single man.

Heracles was ordered to visit the Amazons and bring back a gift for the daughter of Eurystheus: the golden girdle or belt belonging to Hippolyta, the Amazonian queen. Having falsely won the love of Hippolyta so that she gave him the girdle as a love-token, Heracles cold-bloodedly killed her and most of her followers.

Heracles' tenth assignment was to bring back the magnificent cattle of Geryon. The latter, who refused to part with his cattle, was a formidable opponent in battle; he split above the waist into three bodies, and thus had six hands.

Heracles waited to shoot at Geryon until he had manoeuvred himself into a position to one side; then he let fly one powerful arrow, which shot through all three bodies one after another. The cattle then were his, although he took a very long time getting them home and encountered many adventures on the way.

One of his deeds on the homeward journey was to split the rock at the western end of the Mediterranean into the Pillars named after him, as a memorial of his exploits.

The final two labours were the most difficult.

One was to fetch apples from the orchard guarded by the Hesperides. In this orchard or garden was kept the golden apple tree presented by Earth as a wedding gift to Hera, and it was guarded not only by the lovely Hesperides, but by a dragon.

Heracles had no idea where the Garden of the Hesperides was, and he spent a long time roaming the corners of Europe before he found it at the western end of the Mediterranean. Nearby stood Atlas, who had been punished for leading the Titan forces against Zeus by having to stand forever with the sky on his shoulders. Heracles readily killed the dragon, following instructions he had been given by a sea-god, then held the sky for Atlas for a few minutes while the Titan, glad of a few minutes' respite from his burden, fetched the golden apples.

However, Heracles had not bargained on Atlas' desire to remain free.

"You can stay here," the Titan mockingly told him, "and hold up the sky for a while, and I will take the apples back for you."

Heracles knew full well that Atlas would never return, so he thought quickly.

"All right, you may go," he said. "But since I am going to have to stand here for a long time, take the sky for just one moment while I make my lion-skin into a pad for my shoulders."

Atlas trustingly took back the sky, and Heracles, merry at the success of his trick, hastened back to Eurystheus with the apples from the Garden of the Hesperides.

On the return trip he wandered to the far-off Caucasus, and set Prometheus free from his torment.

The final labour involved going to that most feared of all places, the realm of Hades, and bringing up the dread three-headed watchdog Cerberus.

When Heracles reached the underworld, Hades told him that he could take the dog only if he could overcome him without using any weapons. This made the task almost impossible, for Cerberus not only had three heads, each furnished with razor-sharp teeth, but the ruff on each of the three necks was made of poison snakes, and his tail had a knife-like barb on the end.

Heracles resolutely grasped the dog around the throat, just below where it forked into three. The writhing snakes were unable to reach his wrists, and the invulnerable skin of the Nemean lion prevented the barbed tail from wounding him. Before long, Cerberus was overcome, and Heracles triumphantly bore him to the upper world, the twelve labours accomplished at last.

After a lifetime full of adventure, Heracles finally met his end as the result of a base trick.

An evil centaur, Nessus, had once tried to steal Heracles' wife, Deianeira. When Heracles rescued his wife, the centaur brewed a bitter vengeance. As a supposed token of friendship, Nessus gave to Deianeira some magic wool, which he told her to weave into a shirt for Heracles. This wool had been touched with Nessus' own blood, and if Heracles wore it, he would never be unfaithful to his wife—or so the Centaur told Deianeira.

Some time later, Heracles fell in love with another young woman and went to visit her. Discovering where her husband was going, Deianeira hurriedly sent the shirt she had woven after him. After sending the messenger, with orders not to rest until he had caught up with her husband and had given him the shirt, Deianeira noticed a bit of wool from the shirt which had dropped to the ground. To her horror, it burst into flames before her eyes, and burned with an undying intensity.

Deianeira now realized that she had been tricked by the evil Nessus, and killed herself.

Meanwhile, Heracles was delighted to receive a gift from his wife, and donned the attractive shirt immediately. No sooner did he pull it over his head than it began to burn. In agony, he tried to pull it off again, but it would not be removed. Soon Heracles' flesh was afire, but since he was immortal, he could not die.

His agony was unendurable, and finally he called for a funeral pyre to be lit, and placed himself upon it. When his mortal part had all been burned away, he rose to Mount Olympus, where he was received with delight by Zeus and the other gods—all except Hera, who, however, was by now convinced that she had better lay aside her vengeance.

Heracles was made the porter of Mount Olympus, and lived forever with the gods, having proved himself the greatest hero of all time.

VOYAGES

Three of the greatest myth groups deal with perilous voyages made by ancient heroes. The most famous, of course, is Homer's tale of the ten-year homeward voyage of Odysseus, and parts of it were adapted by Virgil to his story of the arduous voyage to Italy made by Aeneas and his Trojan band.

According to legend, the voyage of Jason and his Argonauts to the east was made before these others. Jason was supposed to have been a contemporary of Heracles, and thus to have lived at least one generation before the Trojan war.

Although the Greeks were a sea-faring people, their methods of navigation were crude and their ships small. Many a seaman was lost, even when the voyage was a relatively short and safe one. To them, anyone who would attempt a voyage which took him far out of sight of land, and which lasted for a long time, was a hero.

THE QUEST OF
THE GOLDEN FLEECE

HE rightful king of a small Greek land had been deposed by his own kinsman, a ruthless half-brother named Pelias. To protect his newly-won power, Pelias then cold-bloodedly murdered every known claimant to the throne. Despite these desperate measures, he lived in fear that some day someone younger and stronger would depose and kill him in turn. His fear was not lessened by an oracle who warned him, "Beware of the man with one sandal!"

The years passed peacefully enough, but eventually the dreaded man with only one sandal did appear at the king's court. His appearance and manly bearing caused considerable stir at the court, and no one, not even Pelias, was surprised to hear his identity.

He was Jason, the son of the old deposed king; a son who had been smuggled out of the kingdom in the times of danger, and had been brought up by a wise centaur in a far-off land. Now that he was grown, he claimed his father's throne for himself.

So commanding was the young man's presence that Pelias was afraid to deny him before all the court. Quickly, he thought of a plan to rid himself of the threat forever.

"Years ago," he told Jason, "a boy who was your own cousin was to be sacrificed to bring an end to famine. He escaped miraculously, for a golden ram descended to the place of sacrifice, took the boy on his back, and bore him to the land of Colchis. The boy later died, and his soul has never found rest so far from home. His ghost tells us that if we bring the fleece of that golden ram back to Greece, he will find rest.

"If you will do this service to the soul of a kinsman, then you, Jason, will receive my throne. Go to Colchis, and bring back the golden fleece!"

Jason could not refuse to do kindness to a dead kinsman, although the task was to be performed only with great danger. His courage was bolstered, however, by a notion that perhaps the goddess Hera would help him, for it was through her intervention that he had found his way to the palace. He had been walking beside a river when an old, wrinkled crone had stopped him, pleading for help across. When he had willingly carried her across, although he lost a sandal on the way, she had revealed herself as Hera. She was angry with Pelias, she told him, for he had offended her; Jason was to go and claim what was rightfully his.

Jason's first step in preparing to retrieve the golden fleece was to gather a band of heroes from all parts of Greece. All who came to join him were distinguished for bravery or cunning, and a few became famous for all time: Heracles, the twins Castor and Polydeuces, Orpheus the musician, and even a woman, Atalanta of Calydon, the huntress who was surer of aim and fleeter of foot than any of her countrymen.

To carry the band to Colchis, Jason commissioned a ship from the master-builder Argus. The ship was named the *Argo*, for its builder, and its band of adventurers took the name *Argonauts.*

Many adventures befell the Argonauts in their eastward voyage to Colchis. On one occasion, they had to elude the Clashing Rocks which, shrouded in mist, guarded a narrow passage and crushed anyone who tried to pass through. The Argonauts released a dove, and the rocks tried to crush it; the bird escaped with the loss of only a few tail-feathers, and as the rocks were drawing apart for another try, Jason and his crew sped through. Later they encountered the Amazons, a race of warrior women, and the savage, birdlike Harpies. Tragedy beset them, too: Heracles' best friend, Hylas, vanished without a trace, and several members of the party met violent deaths.

Finally, in spite of all obstacles, they reached their goal.

Colchis was under the rule of a king named Aeëtes, whose court the Argonauts approached peacefully and courteously. When they had been duly received, Jason explained his mission to the king.

Aeëtes was unwilling to let the fabulous fleece go from his possession; yet he hesitated to insult a guest.

"You may have the fleece," he said finally, "if you can prove your worth by carrying out several small tasks."

Jason, he said, must yoke two fire-breathing bulls which were ravaging the land, and with them plow a certain field and sow it with the teeth of a serpent.

The task was even harder than it sounded. The king knew that

Jason would probably perish in the attempt to yoke the bulls. If he did manage to survive, he would get a shock when he sowed the teeth of the serpent, for armed men were to spring up from each tooth, ready to kill.

But while the king was issuing instructions to Jason, his daughter, the princess Medea, had joined him. At first sight she fell in love with the newcomer, and, although she knew her father's purpose, stole out that night to find Jason.

When she met him, she boldly proposed a bargain.

"I will help you get the golden fleece if you will take me away to be your wife," she said. Jason readily agreed, for Medea was endowed with a magical beauty.

The princess anointed Jason with a potion, and sent him out to do the tasks her father had assigned. Jason discovered that the liquid made him invulnerable, and he was easily able to capture and harness the bulls. He had to rely on his own wits for the second part of the test, however: when the armed men sprang from the serpent's teeth, he threw a stone into their midst to set them fighting against one another, and soon all were dead.

Medea then led Jason to the place where the fleece hung, and she herself subdued the guardian dragon, for she was a witch-maiden.

With the fleece in their possession at last, Jason and the Argonauts prepared to sail for home. Medea sailed with them, and her young brother as well. Jason soon learned why Medea had insisted on taking this youth with them, for, without a trace of regret, she murdered him and calmly cut up his body as the Argo was leaving the harbour. When the ships of Aeëtes were seen in pursuit, Medea cast the pieces of her brother's corpse one by one over the side. The pursuers allowed their quarry to escape while they took time to collect the pieces of the dead prince.

Medea had already done great service to Jason, although doing so demanded monstrous crimes. She was to be of even greater use to him. There was one time, on the way home, when she actually saved all the Argonauts from the clutches of Talus, a bronze giant on the isle of Crete; Medea lulled him to sleep, then pulled a plug in his ankle, which allowed all his life-fluid to flow away.

When the Argonauts, after a long and arduous voyage, finally reached their destination with the golden fleece, Jason discovered that Pelias had made plans to kill him.

"Let me take the city for you," pleaded Medea.

Her words sounded foolish, but knowing what strange and terrible powers the young woman possessed, Jason agreed to let her try.

Medea dressed herself as an old woman and, carrying an image of the goddess Artemis, managed to get by the guards of the city. She went directly to the palace of Pelias and demanded to see the king.

"The goddess Artemis has sent me to you, so that you may be made young once more," she told the startled king. Unbelieving, he asked for proof of her power.

For the first proof, Medea discarded her disguise of a crone, and told the king that she had just been rejuvenated into a young and beautiful woman. He could hardly believe his eyes; to convince him further, she performed a gruesome ritual before him.

Taking a very old ram, she killed it and threw pieces of it into a cauldron of boiling brew.

"This is the way the goddess makes her chosen ones young again," she told the king. "Look!"—and from a hiding place she pulled a frisky lamb, which she pretended was the old ram young again.

Convinced at last, Pelias allowed Medea to approach him and, reassuring him that he soon would be young and strong, she killed him and cut his body in pieces.

With his rival dead, Jason entered the city won for him by Medea, and in spite of his revulsion at her crimes, he married the princess.

IN HISTORY

This story is not the only mention of the golden fleece in myth and legend. It occurs again in the story of Psyche, and in both stories is regarded as an object of great value.

Many scholars have speculated on the actual object of such a voyage as the one of the *Argo*, and have produced a tremendous variety of suggestions. There is one theory, however, by which the object may actually have been golden fleece; in some areas of Asia Minor and the Black Sea lands, natives laid fleeces upon the river beds to catch alluvial gold. The sight of drying fleeces sparkling with bits of gold may have been responsible for Greek raids upon these lands.

ECHOES IN ART

Painters and sculptors have found in the tales of mortals of myth and legend fit subjects for their art, although such stories have never held the appeal for artists that the tales of the gods have.

A famous painting by Raoux (Louvre, Paris) shows Galatea being brought to life. Aphrodite, accompanied by Eros, turtle-doves, and beings who closely resemble angels, touches the lovely statue to life, while Pygmalion falls back amazed.

The myth of Narcissus is depicted in many well-known works. Perhaps the most famous is the one by Poussin (Louvre, Paris), in which Narcissus is stretched upon the river bank, while behind him, unnoticed by the languishing youth, sit Eros and a disconsolate nymph. Lorrain's painting of Echo (National Gallery, London) shows the unhappy nymph, tiny in a magical and romantic landscape, lying hidden amid the trees.

The essence of the story of Daedalus and Icarus is caught in a painting by Van Dyck (Art Gallery of Toronto). It shows a wise and wrinkled Daedalus cautioning Icarus not to fly too high, lest he fall and drown.

The story of Psyche has been told in pictures by Raphael and his school in a series of wall-paintings in the Farnesina Palace, Rome. The adventures of Jason are recounted in a fanciful series painted by the followers of Pesellino, now in New York's Metropolitan Museum of Art.

As numerous as the tales of Heracles are the paintings representing him. Every episode has been represented as visualized by several, sometimes many, different artists.

PART THREE

THE EPICS

HE wedding of Peleus and Thetis was to be a gala affair. All the gods and goddesses had been invited except one. The bloodthirsty goddess of discord, Eris, had been left out; and little wonder, for she always caused trouble. She was the twin sister of the god of war, and her favourite pastime was sowing seeds of strife wherever she went.

But a goddess's vanity was not to be trifled with. While all the guests were celebrating at the wedding feasts, the slighted Eris was plotting. The plan she devised was destined to throw not only Olympus, but the whole world, into confusion.

In the midst of the festivities, a hush fell over the assembly as the uninvited goddess appeared suddenly among the guests. Her lip curled in scorn as she drew herself up to her full majestic height and disdainfully tossed down an apple—a golden apple, inscribed simply, *To the Fairest*. Then vengeful Eris disappeared as quickly as she had come.

The wedding guests went wild. For whom had Eris intended the apple? Almost every goddess claimed to be the most beautiful and thus worthy of the prize. However, the contenders for the honour soon were narrowed to only three, the great queens of heaven: Hera, Athene, and Aphrodite.

The three goddesses appealed to Zeus to settle the matter. But Zeus knew that if he admitted one of the goddesses to be more beautiful than the others, he would have to suffer the wrath of the offended two. Trying to avoid all six proud but anxious eyes fixed upon him, he made a quick and cautious decision.

"You are all so beautiful," he said carefully. "To choose the fairest would be impossible—for me. But if you go to Mount Ida, you will find a young man there who is an expert in these matters. His name is Paris, and he is as wise as he is handsome. Hurry, so that you can catch him before he leads his herds home for the night."

Actually, Zeus knew much more about Paris than the young man did himself. Paris thought himself to be a simple herdsman, for he had lived as long as he could remember on the slopes of Mount Ida tending his father's cattle. However, he was really a prince, the son of Priam, King of Troy.

Just before Paris's birth, seers had told Priam that the child about to be born would cause the downfall of Troy. Such a risk was, of course, far too great for Priam, and the saddened king gave orders for the child to be killed. At the last minute, however, the herdsman who had been commissioned to do the deed could not bring himself to kill the baby. Instead, he took him to his mountain home and raised him as his own son.

Paris grew to be tall, athletic, and well-proportioned. He was the most attractive youth within a thousand miles of Mount Olympus, and every maiden's heart skipped a beat when he glanced her way.

The young herdsman was astounded when the three magnificent goddesses appeared before him.

"What in heaven's name do you want with me, divine ladies?"

"Almighty Zeus commands you, Paris, to select the loveliest goddess of these three," replied Hermes, who was carrying the golden apple. Zeus had been too wise to entrust the prize to any one of the vain and jealous contestants.

Of course, Paris knew better than to disobey a command of the king of the gods. Insisting modestly that he was quite unequal to such a responsibility, he set himself to the difficult but pleasant task of assessing the beauties of the three goddesses.

It was not an easy decision, and Athene, Hera, and Aphrodite knew it. Each was determined to win the trophy designating her as the most beautiful goddess in Olympus, but deep in her heart each was afraid that the young herdsman would select one of the others.

Hera was the first to draw Paris aside for a moment.

"Paris, you must know that the apple was really meant for me," she whispered. "If you judge me the fairest, you will become lord of all Asia, and the richest man in the world."

The offer was tempting. Before Paris had time to answer, however, his attention was caught by the tall, warlike Athene.

"Give me the apple, Paris," she said. "In return, I promise that you shall conquer the whole world, if you like. And I'll make you the wisest man in the whole world, too!"

Aphrodite had been waiting quietly, a little smile on her lips.

"I will give you Helen of Sparta, the most beautiful woman in the world, for your wife," she said simply.

And Paris, who was a romantic man, took the apple and without another second's hesitation awarded it to Aphrodite, the goddess of love.

Aphrodite danced back to Mount Olympus with her prize, and from that day on, she was the friend and protector of Paris, the young prince who thought himself a simple herdsman. But the decision which won for Paris the thanks of one goddess brought him the hatred of the other two, and the wrath of Athene and Hera pursued Paris and all those associated with him until the day of his death.

The woman whom Aphrodite had promised to Paris was indeed the most beautiful woman in the world.

So perfect was she, in fact, that when the time had come for her to be married, every king, prince, and lord in all Greece had sought her hand. All had come to the home of her father Tyndareus (or step-father, for some say that Helen was the daughter of Zeus himself), bearing gold and jewels and other expensive gifts, to ask for Helen as queen.

The presence of so many suitors put Tyndareus in a difficult position. He knew quite well which of the princes he wanted as a son-in-law, but he was afraid to name him. The others would be jealous, he thought; all were powerful, and any could take revenge. The easiest thing to do was to delay.

For months, the kings and princes of Greece stayed at the palace of Helen. Her father Tyndareus never hinted who was to be the husband of his lovely daughter. Finally, a man named Odysseus sought out Tyndareus.

"There is another woman that I'd like to marry just as much as your daughter," he said, "so I'll step out of the race. But I can tell you how to solve your problem."

Tyndareus listened eagerly to Odysseus' plan. The thing to do, he was told, was to gather all the suitors together, and make them all swear to respect Tyndareus' decision. Furthermore, each had to swear to come to the aid of both Helen and her chosen husband, if the need should ever arise.

The plan worked. Each of the lords of Greece took a solemn oath to protect Helen forever, and Tyndareus at last felt free to name the man of his choice. The man was Menelaus of Sparta, and Helen became his wife and queen of Sparta.

PARIS AND HELEN

THE mind of young Paris was haunted by the visit of the three goddesses. Especially he remembered Aphrodite, to whom he had awarded the title of fairest of the goddesses; try as he might, he could not forget for a moment the promise she had made in return. The memory both delighted and troubled him. Certainly, having the world's loveliest woman for his wife was an exciting prospect, but he could not understand how he, who spent all his days with his father's cows on Mount Ida, could ever meet such a lady. Not only was she beautiful, but a queen of a far-away land!

Perhaps Paris believed, deep in his heart, that if only he could leave the mountains and become a part of the glamorous, sophisticated life in Troy, his dreams and Aphrodite's promise might come true. When messengers of King Priam came to the mountain one day to choose a bull to take part in a great annual festival at court, Paris was seized by an irresistible desire to follow them back to the city.

Once there, he decided to make as much of the visit as possible. All the young men of the city were taking part in competitions of strength and skill; he would take part too!

The first competition was a boxing match. Young Paris had never been trained in boxing, as had the young men of the court; but what he lacked in skill he made up in courage. He made short work of his opponents, and the cheers of the crowd echoed from the towers of Troy when the champion's crown was placed on the head of the excited young stranger.

Among the boxers defeated by Paris were several of the sons of Priam. The princes of Troy were supposed to be the strongest and bravest of all Trojan youth, and they felt a surge of resentment against the brash herdsman who dared challenge them in their own festival games.

When a second crown was awarded Paris for winning one of the foot races, the princes exchanged meaningful glances. When yet a third trophy, again for racing, was given the young man, a blind rage swept over the defeated princes. Quickly, instinctively, they leaped to kill their hated rival. Before the crowd had time to stop them, the Trojan princes had blocked all exits from the arena. Swords drawn, faces contorted with anger, two of the youths raced towards Paris. Bewildered, defenceless, he waited—

"Stop!" A voice rang through the hushed arena.

"Do not harm him! He is your brother!"

It was the old herdsman from Mount Ida, who had followed Paris to the city. Bowing low, he turned to Priam, who had half-risen from his throne and was staring at the young champion.

"Most mighty king," the old herdsman said, "this is your son."

And Priam remembered the child he had regretfully abandoned to its death, remembered the herdsman to whom he had given the unhappy duty, remembered all except an old, ominous prophecy. Perhaps he even recognized something of himself as he had been long ago, in the handsome youth before him.

His eyes filling with tears, Priam rose to welcome his son.

*   *   *

Life in the great palace of Troy was not at all displeasing to the new prince. Memories of the simple, honest life of a herdsman faded quickly; Paris discovered, instead, that he had a taste for comfort and luxury and elegance of living. Troy offered pleasures he never knew existed, and under their influence, the innocent mountain lad became sophisticated.

Life was so good that the promise made by a goddess long before seemed remote and unreal. But though a mortal may forget, a goddess never does; and one day, driven by forces of which he knew nothing, Prince Menelaus of Sparta arrived at the court of Troy. His mission was simple; he had been ordered by an oracle to make sacrifices at Troy, and the visit would be short.

At the sight of the Spartan, Paris remembered Aphrodite's promise, his own old dreams, and all the wonderful things he had heard of the beauty of Queen Helen of Sparta. Without a qualm of conscience, the sly young man managed to win from Menelaus an invitation to visit his domain.

Queen Helen had no choice; Aphrodite had doomed her. The moment she laid eyes on the visiting Trojan prince, she adored him. She tried to hide her feelings from her husband, and perhaps succeeded too well, for Menelaus, blind to what was happening, decided to take a trip. He asked his queen to entertain Paris during his absence.

Helen could resist no longer. On the very night of her husband's departure, she eloped with Paris, and together they sailed to Troy.

Silently the people of Troy stared at the horizon.

It was true. The wild, terrible words shouted through the streets by a half-crazed messenger were true. Those long black forms slipping through the waves were ships—Greek ships. The disaster that they had all feared was happening. The Greeks were coming to take Helen home.

In silence they watched. They counted the ships as they became visible . . . twenty . . . fifty . . . a hundred . . . a thousand! Would they never stop coming?

It was war.

Meanwhile, the heroes of Greece were watching the battlements of Troy emerge through the mists of distance. Almost all were there in the ships—all the lords and princes who had sworn a solemn oath to come to the defence of Helen if she were in trouble.

Menelaus was there, of course. Unmoving, he stood in the prow of the foremost ship, straining his eyes towards the city which had once welcomed him and which now sheltered his faithless wife.

With him was his brother, Agamemnon. This great king had been reluctant to make war which would take hundreds, perhaps thousands of lives, just for the sake of a woman. But the woman was his brother's wife, and for his brother's sake, he could not refuse. There was another factor, too; Helen was the sister of Agamemnon's own queen, Clytemnestra, who lacked her younger sister's extraordinary beauty but was a woman of indomitable will.

The Trojan expedition had already brought heartbreak to Agamemnon. Just as it was due to sail for Troy, the Greek fleet was becalmed and forced to remain in harbour. Precious time slipped by, until finally Agamemnon was informed of the terrible price demanded for raising a wind. Artemis had been offended, and her wrath would be assuaged only by the sacrifice of Agamemnon's youngest daughter, Iphigeneia.

The vision of his daughter upon the sacrifice block flashed before his eyes now, as the towers of Troy took form before him. He wondered if the bloody deed would prove worthwhile.

And there was Odysseus, the wily one. He had not wanted to come on the expedition either; when Agamemnon and Menelaus had sought him in his kingdom of Ithaca, he had pretended to be out of his mind. He had yoked a donkey and an ox together, put on a peasant's cap, and had let the visiting kings find him, plowing and sowing salt in the furrows. However, he had been outmanoeuvred by the visitors, for one of them had snatched Odysseus' baby from safety and thrown him in the path of the plow. When Odysseus quickly turned aside to keep from killing his child, he showed himself to be sane. Bound by honour and by his promise, he joined the expedition.

In other ships were such great Greeks as Nestor, the wise king of Pylus who had ruled over three generations of men; Big Ajax, the giant of the army, who was strong and handsome and almost impossible to wound; Little Ajax, who was small, but the swiftest runner of them all; and hundreds of other great names.

The greatest of all was Achilles.

Of all the Greeks, Achilles was the strongest, the best fighter, and the best-loved hero. When a child, he had been dipped in the sacred waters of the Styx by his immortal mother. This dipping made him invulnerable, or impervious to wounds, except for the tiny spot on his heel where his mother's fingers had held him and prevented the water from touching the skin.

IN HISTORY

For two thousand years, men believed the tale of the Trojan war to be a delightful fantasy and nothing more.

In the nineteenth century, however, a young German lad named Heinrich Schliemann, who heard the tales as a child, dreamed of a day when he would stand where his heroes Hector and Achilles had once fought. Years later, when by a remarkable chain of circumstances Schliemann had become a very rich man, he decided to realize his dream and find ancient Troy.

The scholarly world laughed when the amateur archaeologist set out for Asia Minor to discover a city which they were sure had never existed. Schliemann ignored them, and let folk tradition guide him to a Turkish hill called Hissarlik, which seemed to fit Homer's details of the site of Troy.

As he dug, a city emerged, and another, and another. Schliemann had found Troy—not one, but a whole series of cities, each built upon the ruins of the preceding one. Modern research has decided that the seventh city was Homer's Troy.

The traditional date given for the destruction of Troy is 1184 B.C., which is probably within a century of the true date. Thus Homer's stories, put into poetry several centuries later, reflect both the ancient Trojan civilization which survived only in folk memory and the Greek civilization, called Mycenaean, of Homer's own day.

Homer's Troy probably did fall in a war with the Greeks. By examining the position of Troy on the map, you will see that it lay near a valuable trade route. Modern scholars believe that the Trojan war was really a trade war.

Two other historical speculations are worthy of attention. First, it is quite likely that the war lasted an extraordinarily long time, for excavations show that the city had great walls which would make capture almost impossible. Secondly, it may be true that for this particular trade war many of the little kingdoms of Greece joined in an alliance. If so, this was most unusual, for they did not ally again for about seven hundred years, and then only in short periods of crisis.

ECHOES IN LITERATURE

The story of the sacrifice of Iphigeneia has been told in several versions. The most famous is *Iphigeneia in Tauris*, by Euripides, great dramatist of fifth-century Athens. His tale takes a turn quite different from Homer's, for according to Euripides, Artemis took pity on the girl at the last moment and took her away. In her place was left a deer, ready for the sacrifice.

Iphigeneia was taken to Tauris, now called the Crimea, where she became a priestess in the temple of Artemis, in charge of consecrating Greek prisoners to be executed. Eventually one of those who came into her hands was her own brother, Orestes. At the last moment, Iphigeneia discovered his identity and quickly planned their escape together. They were saved from capture and terrible punishment by the intervention of Athene.

Poets have usually emphasized the pathos of the sacrifice of Iphigeneia, portraying her as a happy girl, full of excitement over the prospect of marriage, then scarcely able to believe the terrible fate her father has planned for her. Among poems of the sacrifice are Landon's *Iphigeneia and Agamemnon* and Tennyson's *A Dream of Fair Women*.

Two of the most famous lines in English literature concern a vision of Helen and of the assembling of the ships to set sail for Troy.

Faust, the scientist who, in Marlowe's drama *The Tragical History of Dr. Faustus*, had bargained with the devil, selling his soul in return for all knowledge, received a visit from Helen. Overwhelmed by her beauty, he cried:

> *Is this the face that launched a thousand ships,*
> *And burnt the topless towers of Ilium?*

HOMER

The authorship of the *Iliad* and *Odyssey* is one of the world's greatest literary puzzles.

Tradition claims that the stories were told by Homer, a blind poet, but no one, even in ancient times, had any clear knowledge of this author. Although seven different Greek cities claimed to have been his birthplace, none could offer any historical evidence that the poet had lived there or had sung any of his poetry there.

Then, about one hundred and fifty years ago, a scholar wrote a book which shook the world of classical scholarship. He announced that there could not possibly have been any such person as Homer; there were simply too many elements, too many different types of story, contained in the epics. "Homer" had to be regarded as a general name for the unknown hundreds of bards who composed sections of the stories which were not put together until much later.

This theory was believed until recent decades, when scholars began to find a peculiar unity in the structure of the epics. Most of them now believe that the works were, after all, the product of one person, or at most two, one who wrote the *Iliad* and one the *Odyssey*.

However, some mystery still exists about just when this poet lived. Many references to weapons, buildings, and ways of life in the *Iliad* force scholars to conclude that Homer did not live until perhaps as late as the eighth century B.C. Yet if this is so, the mystery deepens; those were historical times, and if such a great poet lived then, how is it that we have no historical records of him?

The other important historical fact that has been fairly well established is that Homer was actually telling stories which had been passed down for several centuries. He may have been separated by five hundred years from the events which he describes, yet sometimes he describes with astonishing accuracy the civilization which has been concluded to be the one called Mycenaean—the one which flourished during the greatest power of the city of Mycenae.

Because he describes so well things which he could not possibly have seen, many people believe that perhaps not a single line, or a single phrase, was original with Homer. Be that as it may, the poet still wove thousands of lines and dozens of incidents into the greatest epics ever produced by man.

THE ILIAD

The *Iliad* recounts certain events which took place near the end of the siege of Troy, a city in Asia Minor.

The war for the city of Troy actually lasted for ten years, but Homer's story does not begin until after nine years had passed. Nor does he complete the story; he concludes with the funeral of the Trojan hero Hector, and never reaches such well-known parts of the Trojan tale as the death of Achilles, or the building of the wooden horse.

The central character of Homer's story is Achilles, the Greek hero who believed that the others had insulted his honour, and who sulked in his tent until it was almost too late.

THE ANGER OF ACHILLES

A man and his anger were the cause of the happenings of the terrible tenth year of the siege of Troy, the last year that proud city stood.

The bitter rancour of Achilles burst forth over a girl and mounted over his treatment by the great king Agamemnon.

Among the Trojan captives taken by the Greeks was Chryseis, daughter of a priest of Apollo, and so lovely that she had been taken as a prize by Agamemnon himself. When her father came to the king, humbly offering a ransom for the return of Chryseis, Agamemnon rudely sent him away.

Denied his daughter, the old priest prayed that night to Apollo:

"If I have ever done good for thee, Apollo of the silver bow, bestow on me this boon: make the Greeks pay dearly for my tears!"

Apollo heard the prayers of his priest, and heeded them. Burning at the insult which had been offered, he strode angrily down from Olympus and, drawing near the Greek tents, let fly his arrows of pestilence. For nine days he remained there, shooting arrow after arrow of disease into the camp. Every arrow hit a Greek soldier, and soon the air was filled with the moans of the dying and the stench from the pyres of the dead.

Since the men were unable to fight, the great and respected Achilles called the generals to a council meeting where they persuaded a seer to tell them the cause of the disease and death. When they had heard of Apollo's wrath, all agreed that Agamemnon had to return his captive.

The great king rose to his feet, eyes flashing with rage.

"What! Will you all try to cheat me of my prize! Even you, Achilles

—you say so easily that my captive, whom I like better than my own wife, is to be taken from me! Very well! If it must be done, I shall send her back—but I will take your captive, the beautiful Briseis, in her place!"

Achilles could not allow his fondness for a captive to destroy the Greek army, as Agamemnon had almost done. But the fury began to burn within him.

"You coward!" he snarled to Agamemnon. "All you can do is order men to fight, while you yourself hide in your tent. Your heart is as soft as a fawn's! Take Briseis, then, but listen well to my oath: the time will come when all Greeks will regret your insults to me.

"There will be a time, when Greeks are falling like flies before the Trojans, when all of you will cry for Achilles, the bravest man of the Greek army!"

That very day, messengers from Agamemnon led Briseis from the tent of Achilles.

Achilles was not the only one who was enraged by the highhanded action of greedy Agamemnon. His mother, Thetis the sea-nymph, was so offended at the treatment of her son's dignity that she went straight to Zeus, pleading with him to look with disfavour upon the Greeks, who had so dishonoured her son. Reluctantly, for he did not like to take sides, Zeus agreed to help the Trojans defeat the army of Greece.

And so, while the war raged on and the gods of Olympus themselves began to take an interest, the great Greek hero Achilles refused to fight, and sulked in his tent.

THE WAR ON OLYMPUS

ITHOUT the tremendous power of Achilles to bolster them, the Greek army began to fall apart. As the attackers' strength waned, the Trojans took heart and grew strong.

They had several powerful allies to help them.

Zeus, influenced by Thetis, favoured the Trojans. So, of course, did Apollo, whose priest had been offended by Agamemnon and who had a special affection for the Trojan prince Hector. Probably the most deeply involved of the goddesses was Aphrodite, who had stirred up the whole affair by promising Helen of Sparta to Paris of Troy; one of the Trojan heroes, Aeneas, was her son.

Ares, the war god, was in love with Aphrodite and fought on her side. Artemis the huntress sided with her brother Apollo, and so she too helped the Trojans.

The Greeks had their Olympian champions as well. Hera and Athene, offended by Paris, hated the Trojans, and Hera especially was so bitter that she went far out of her way to help the Greeks. Poseidon, lord of the sea, favoured the Greeks because as a sea-faring people they spent long hours atop his realm.

At length Hera grew distressed by the turn of the war, and she resorted to trickery to aid her beloved Greeks. To make her husband, the king of the gods, forget the Trojan cause for a time, Hera dressed herself in her most glorious robes and spent hours in her chamber making herself beautiful. As a final touch, she put on Aphrodite's magic girdle of charms. Then she went to Zeus.

Zeus was so enchanted by her appearance that he embraced her, and Hera poured sleep upon him. When Zeus forgot his involvement with the war below and closed his eyes in slumber, the Trojan forces on the plains below began to lose their strength.

HECTOR AND
ANDROMACHE

THE hero of the Trojans was Hector, one of the sons of Priam, a stalwart fighter who was also a man of kind heart. He, of all the Trojans, had been kindest to poor Helen, who had brought such sorrow upon the city; yet he was the bravest in his land's defense.

The day came when Hector knew he must say goodbye, perhaps forever, to his wife Andromache. She ran to meet him near the gates of the city, as he was leaving to go to the battlefield on the plains. In her arms she carried their little son Astyanax. Tears coursed down the cheeks of Andromache.

"Have you no pity, Hector?" she cried. "Soon I will be not your wife, but your widow, and it would be better to die, for there will be no happiness in the world without you."

Her words touched the heart of Hector, and he tried to comfort her, but Andromache continued.

"You brought me from a far land, and you are all I have. You are my husband, and my parents and brothers too; do not leave me and your son alone in the world! Stay here, where we are together, where we are safe!"

Hector answered her slowly.

"How could I show my face, Andromache, if I hid like a coward? I know in my heart that some day I shall perish, and all Troy too, and I fear you may be taken as a captive; yet even knowing this, I must leave you to go and fight for my city."

Saying this, he reached out to take his little son in his arms once more, but the baby was frightened by the fierce plume on his father's helmet, and shrank away, sobbing. Hector smiled sadly at the child's fear, and took off his helmet. Then the boy came willingly to his arms, and Hector prayed:

"O Zeus and all the gods! Grant that this child may surpass me, and grant that he may one day rule Troy. May he be praised above his father, and may he always bring joy to his mother's heart!"

Then he turned to Andromache, and spoke his final words to her.

"Do not grieve, for no one can kill me before the day on which it is ordained that I must die. I have a destiny, and no man can escape his fate."

So saying, he turned and went to the plains of war. Andromache walked slowly to her home, turning often to look at his departing figure, and her tears flowed thick and fast.

IN HISTORY

The stories of heroes reflect, in many cases, the concept of heroism that existed in Homeric times. The Homeric concept was based not on virtue or goodness, but upon honour. The hero was a man who turned his superior powers to the pursuit of honour and the winning of fame. Honour and fame could be won through action: deeds of daring, particularly in adventure and battle. The hero willingly undertook dangerous tasks because through them he could best show his manliness. Thus, an honourable death in battle was to be desired far above a calm and virtuous life at home.

ATROCLUS, the dearest friend of Achilles, saw with despair how the loss of his friend had affected the Greek army. He had chosen to stay with Achilles, to uphold his friend against the insult he had received from Agamemnon, but the time had come when he could no longer with honour stay away from the fight. He pleaded with Achilles to return to lead the Greeks.

Achilles appeared touched by his words.

"Perhaps the time has come to let bygones be bygones," he said. "Yet how my spirit burns when I think of Agamemnon, who took my prize from me as if I were a foreigner without any rights!

"Tonight, I will stay with my ships, for the Trojan fire has reached them and they must be defended. But you, Patroclus, go to fight! Fight well, and return victorious!"

And to help his friend, he gave Patroclus his own armour.

Patroclus went to the front and struck terror into the hearts of the Trojans, who thought that the great champion Achilles had returned. Like a whirlwind he fought, so well that he tossed away the promise he had made to Achilles before leaving, a promise that he would fight only until the rout of the Trojans was started. All his efforts seemed to bring victory closer, and Patroclus fought on. Finally he was face to face with Hector himself.

But all mortal powers were no match for those of the gods. Apollo had been sitting on Olympus watching the dreadful attack of Patroclus, the bloody slaughter of so many Trojans, and could not bear the sight of Hector falling back before the Greek.

Leaping from the skies, he smote Patroclus a mighty blow on the back. The plumed helmet of Achilles rolled in the dust, and the sword of the champion was shattered by the gods. Even Achilles' wonderful armour which Patroclus wore so proudly was stripped from his body. As the Greek stood there, dazed, Hector saw his chance and plunged his spear deep into the body of his enemy.

A cloud of sorrow swept over Achilles when he received word of Patroclus' death. Upon hearing that Hector himself was wearing the armour of Achilles, the hero swept up the dust of the earth and poured it on his head, uttering such a great cry that his mother Thetis heard and came to comfort him.

She heard him cry that he was going to kill Hector, and the words made her tremble, for she knew that her son was fated to die soon after the death of the Trojan prince.

"I must go!" Achilles swore. "I have been sitting here, a burden to the earth, and now my friend has died in my place! Now I will go and find the killer of that dear life, and destroy him. May I bring tears to the eyes of the Trojan women!"

Knowing that she could not dissuade her enraged son, Thetis contented herself by extracting from him one promise. Since Hector was wearing the armour of Achilles, her son needed new; he must wait in his tent one more day, until she brought him marvellous armour made by the smith of the gods, Hephaestus.

The next day, the fateful fight took place.

Hector was ready to meet Achilles, but when he saw the Greek champion descending upon him, his heavenly armour glowing, even the brave heart of the bravest of the Trojans knew fear. Hector could only turn and flee. Beside him, to protect him, ran Apollo.

Away from Achilles he raced, the Greek champion in pursuit. They ran faster than men running a race, for the prize at stake was the life of Hector. Around the walls of Troy they ran, and again, and a third time, Hector managing always to keep just out of reach of Achilles.

When they were beginning to run for the fourth time, Zeus, who was watching with all the other gods and goddesses, took out a golden scale, in which he weighed the fates of the two runners. As all the gods watched, the fate of Achilles rose, while that of Hector sank

114

down to Hades. At that moment, Apollo knew that Hector was doomed, and left his side.

Athene, who greatly favoured the Greeks, saw her opportunity.

She flew to the side of Hector, and assumed the form of one of his brothers. With his brother's voice, she whispered in his ear to stand and fight.

Hector was emboldened by the presence of an ally, and turned to face Achilles at last. But as he lifted his spear, he saw that there was no one beside him, and that it had all been a trick.

"I have been deceived," he cried. "The gods have summoned me, yet I will not die without a blow!"

So saying, he drew his sword. But Achilles, who knew well the armour that Hector was wearing, launched his spear with deadly accuracy; the point of it swept through a small hole in the armour and into Hector's throat.

As he lay dying, Hector begged Achilles to return his body to Priam, but Achilles laughed. Then the soul of Hector left his body, wailing for its lost youth, and flew to Hades.

Achilles pierced the feet of the dead Trojan and tied him by ropes to his chariot. To show his utter contempt for his lifeless opponent, he dragged the body three times around the walls of Troy, then to the Greek camp where, he said, he would leave it out for the dogs.

Finally, old Priam, the once-proud Trojan king, came and humbled himself before the slayer of his son, pleading that he might have the body to bury.

Achilles had been bitter and vengeful, but as he looked at the old man he remembered his own father, and his heart was softened. He bade his servants wash and anoint the body of Hector, so that the dreadful gashes from its terrible treatment might be hidden.

Then Priam took the body of his son home to a saddened and doomed Troy.

Troy was disheartened by the loss of its great champion, and most Trojans sensed that the end was near. Yet there was no going back, no time left for truces and bargains.

The rest of the story is told mainly by Virgil, and by the Greek dramatist Euripides.

More and more, death visited the ranks of both Greeks and Trojans.

As was ordained, the hero Achilles soon met death, an inglorious one at the hands of Paris. Actually, Paris managed to kill the great Greek only with the aid of Apollo, for the god guided an arrow to the one tiny spot in which Achilles could be wounded: the little place on his heel which had been covered by the fingers of his mother Thetis when she dipped him in the waters of the Styx.

The death of Achilles was followed by that of Ajax, who, driven in madness to kill cattle, under the impression that they were his own companions who he thought had insulted him, committed suicide in shame when his sanity returned.

Soon after, Paris himself was mortally wounded. He asked to be taken to a nymph, Oenone, whom he had loved while a simple shepherd, for Oenone had the power to cure any ailment. But the nymph had been hurt by his rejection, and was bitter: she refused to help Paris, and watched him die. Then she too took her own life.

THE WOODEN HORSE

ILY Odysseus finally devised the stratagem which was to win the war.

He had the Greeks build a great wooden horse, big enough to hold a band of men inside its body. He and the other leaders of the Greek forces hid inside, and had the horse drawn by night to the gates of Troy. The rest of the Greeks then sailed out of sight, and hid behind a small off-shore island called Tenedos.

When morning came, the citizens of Troy were amazed. Gone was the Greek camp from the plains. Gone were the Greek ships from the shore. All that remained was a huge wooden horse.

All, that is, except for one man. He was a Greek, whose name was Sinon, and he came to the Trojans begging mercy. He had barely managed to escape his own people, he said, who had been going to sacrifice him to the goddess Athene. The goddess had been angry at an outrage committed by the Greeks in one of her temples, and had demanded the sacrifice. The Greeks had made the horse as an offering, to please the goddess, and had left it before the Trojan gates in hopes that the Trojans would draw the wrath of Athene upon themselves by destroying it.

The Trojans were delighted. The war was over! They had won, and now their city was safe! They even made plans to take the horse into the city and honour it, to please the goddess Athene.

Only two people in all Troy spoke out against the horse. One of these was Cassandra, daughter of King Priam, a prophetess who had once offended the god Apollo and had been doomed to have her prophecies forever disbelieved; the Trojans laughed at her warnings. The other was Laocoön, a priest, who sombrely announced that he feared the Greeks even when they came bearing gifts. As if to punish him, two huge serpents arose from the water nearby, glided straight to the priest, and crushed him and his two children to death, before disappearing into the temple of Athene.

The rejoicing Trojans dragged the horse into the city and wreathed it with garlands. They danced around it, happy for the first time in ten years. Finally, made sleepy with wine and joyful celebration, they went to their homes.

In the dead of night, the Greek leaders opened the trap door in the belly of the horse and crept out. They opened the gates of the city, and let in the rest of their forces, who had sailed back in the darkness.

By morning the best of the Trojan warriors lay dead in the streets, and the city which had once been the proud mistress of the east lay in smoking ruins.

While the rest of the Greeks fought the Trojans, who, rudely aroused from sleep, were at a disadvantage, one, Menelaus, had been about other business. He went straight to the palace, intent upon killing the faithless beauty who had caused ten years of sorrow; but

when his eyes fell upon her face, made older by sorrow but even more
beautiful, his anger melted away. Graciously he knelt before Helen,
and reclaimed her as his queen.

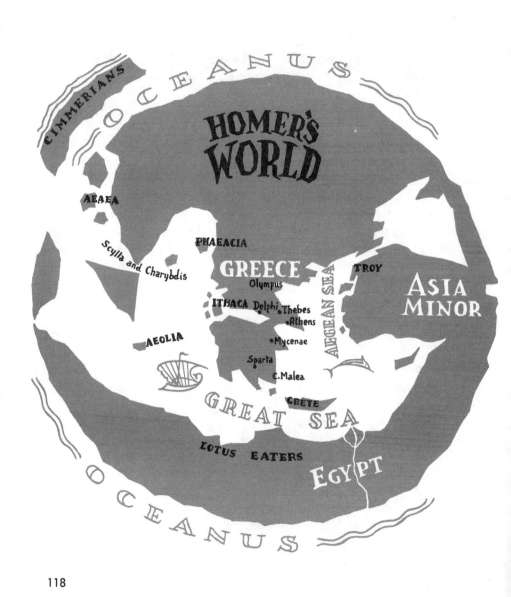

THE ODYSSEY

Homer's *Odyssey* is the first and perhaps the best adventure tale of all time. It has been a favourite for three thousand years.

The *Odyssey* is the story of Odysseus, son of Laertes, who after nine years of battle before the walls of distant Troy, travelled for ten more throughout the ancient world before he arrived home to the rugged isle of Ithaca. Homer tells of the many troubles Zeus laid upon Odysseus and of the many hardships he endured to save his own life and to bring his men safely back to their homes.

The following stories are some of the episodes from the *Odyssey*.

THE LAND OF THE LOTUS-EATERS

FROM Ilium, the ancient name for Troy, the winds carried the twelve sturdy galleys of Odysseus to Ismaros, the land of the Ciconians. There Odysseus destroyed the town and killed its menfolk, but he ordered his followers to spare the women and the cattle. The plunder they divided among themselves.

The wily Odysseus ordered his men to beat a hasty retreat to the ships, but in their exhilaration they would not listen to him. They drank a great deal of wine, and feasted on sheep and cattle which they slaughtered and roasted on the beach. Meanwhile, some of the enemy had escaped. These were joined by other Ciconians from inland towns, and a great battle ensued. The enemy swarmed down from the hills, both infantry and charioteers, and drew up near the ships. All through the morning Odysseus held them off, but several men from each ship were killed, and by noon the rest were forced to withdraw.

Sick at heart but thankful to be alive, they sailed away. Yet this was only the beginning of their troubles.

If Zeus had sent them a hard fate that day, he had not finished his work. Calling upon the North Wind, he dispatched a furious tempest which drove the ships headlong. Night descended from the sky. In the blackness, sails were ripped to shreds before they could be let down, and the helpless crews, in fear of death, rode the bare ships to shore.

Two days later, when the gale subsided, the mariners hoisted new sails and made towards Ithaca. But again the wind caught them as they rounded Cape Malea and drove them past Cythera. For nine more days the ships were battered by foul weather, and on the tenth day the exhausted band made land in what they found to be the country of the Lotus-Eaters, where they went ashore to take in water and to eat.

The natives proved to be very friendly and gave three of the men some of their food, called lotus, to eat. But as soon as they tasted the luscious fruit, they chose to remain in idleness with the lotus-eating natives, and had no intention of returning to the ship or even of returning home. Such was the effect of the honey-sweet lotus.

Odysseus was forced to bind these three men and have them dragged back to the ships before any more of the crew could taste of the succulent fruit and say goodbye to home. Soon they were all on board, bending to their oars, to send the galleys scudding across the sea.

ECHOES IN LITERATURE

In *The Lotus-Eaters*, Tennyson gave a vivid description of the sailors, when they had eaten of the magical fruit of forgetfulness:

> They sat them down upon the yellow sand,
> Between the sun and moon upon the shore;
> And sweet it was to dream of Fatherland,
> Of child, and wife, and slave; but evermore
> Most weary seem'd the sea, weary the oar,
> Weary the wandering fields of barren foam.
> Then someone said, "We will return no more";
> And all at once they sang, "Our island home
> Is far beyond the wave; we will no longer roam."

EFORE long Odysseus and his men reached an island. In the dark of the night they beached their ships and slept soundly until the dawn. All the day they feasted on the meat and delicious wine they had stolen when they took the Ciconian town. The following day, they started to explore.

From the island they could look across to a land where smoke curled from cooking-fires, and they could hear the bleating of sheep and goats. This was to prove to be the country of the Cyclops, a tribe of monstrous one-eyed giants, wild and violent. Each lived in a cave on his own mountain, and each made his own laws for his own family, without regard for his neighbour. The Cyclops neither planted nor plowed, nor did they build ships or visit the cities of the world. They merely tended their flocks and relied on nature to grow wheat, barley, and great bunches of grapes.

Odysseus addressed his men:

"The rest of you stay here while I take my ship and crew to see if these people be friend or foe."

When they reached the land, they could see the mouth of a cave on a headland where flocks of sheep and goats were kept. Odysseus told the rest of the crew to stay with the ship and chose twelve of the best men to come with him. In the cave they found baskets loaded with cheeses, and pens crowded with lambs and young goats. Great pots swam with fresh milk and whey. The men settled down to await the giant's return.

At last he appeared, throwing down a tremendous load of wood with which to cook his supper. Then he picked up a huge boulder and jammed it into the mouth of the cave, and his thunderous voice rang out: "Who are you, and why do you come here? Are you traitors, or are you pirates ready to kill or be killed?"

The men quaked with terror, but Odysseus answered firmly, "We are Achaeans from Troy, who have lost our way home. Since we come on our knees before you, please give us a stranger's due. The almighty Zeus is the protector of strangers."

"What do I care for your gods!" the giant sneered. "We Cyclops are stronger than they!"

And he snatched up two of Odysseus' men, like a pair of puppies, and dashed them to the ground. There they lay, their brains soaking into the earth; then he cut them to pieces and served them for his supper, devouring them like a mountain lion.

Terrified and helpless, the others could only groan and raise their hands to Zeus. Odysseus thought of trying to drive his sword into the monster's breast, but what would be the use with that great rock blocking the exit?

Dawn came. The Cyclops seized two more of the men for his breakfast, then pushed aside the boulder, drove out his flock, and, sealing up the cave mouth, led the animals away to the hills.

But the wily Odysseus had a plan. There in the cave was a tall sapling of green olive-wood that the Cyclops was drying to use as a club. Odysseus cut off a six-foot length, sharpened the end which he charred in the coals of the fire, and hid the pole under the filth on the floor. Then he chose four men to carry out his stratagem.

In the evening when the giant returned with his flock, he once more blocked the entrance. Then he settled down to a supper of two more of the men.

"Have a drink!" Odysseus offered the giant a cup of the wine he had brought. "Wash down that jolly meal of man's mutton with this!"

Three times he filled the cup for the delighted giant, and the strong stuff soon went to the Cyclops' head.

He asked Odysseus his name.

"No Man," Odysseus replied.

"Then No Man shall be the last to be eaten. This shall be my gift to you, stranger," and then the monster fell asleep.

Odysseus then placed the sharpened end of the stake in the ashes, and just when it was about to catch fire, he and his men drove it into the giant's one eye. They twisted it round and round as it sizzled and smoked.

The horrible bellow of the maddened Cyclops brought his neighbours running.

"What on earth is the matter with you, Polyphemus?" they called through the rock.

"No Man is killing me by craft!" roared the Cyclops in reply.

"Well, if no man is killing you, the gods must be putting you in pain!" And the neighbours went away, quite unconcerned.

Odysseus laughed at the success of his trick, but there was no escape from the cave. Although the Cyclops, writhing in agony, had removed the rock from the door, he sat there with hands outspread to catch anyone who might try to go out with the animals.

And so another scheme suggested itself. Odysseus tied the rams together in threes, and under the middle one of each three he tied one of his men. Then he himself curled under the belly of the biggest ram of the flock, clutching the shaggy fleece.

And so they waited for the dawn.

At last morning came, and the animals surged out to pasture, their tormented master blindly pawing their backs as each one left the cave. But he did not discover the men concealed underneath. Finally came the great ram, and Odysseus himself was free.

A short distance from the cave, he dropped to the ground and loosed his companions, who drove the flock back to the ship as fast as they could. Very soon they were under way.

When the ship was about as far off shore as a man could shout and still be heard, Odysseus called out in mockery, "I say, Cyclops, you ate the guests who were in your house, and this is your punishment from Zeus!"

In his anger, Polyphemus wrenched the peak from a rocky crag and heaved it into the sea, causing a giant wave which carried the ship back to the shore.

Odysseus pushed her off again, and bade his men row for their lives. But he could not resist shouting another taunt.

"If any one asks who put out your ugly eye, tell him it was Odysseus, conqueror of Troy, son of Laertes of Ithaca!"

The Cyclops gave a strangled cry. He had been told by a soothsayer that he would one day be blinded by one Odysseus.

"I thought he would be a tall, handsome hero, not a puny weakling like you!"

The wounded monster lifted his hands to heaven:

"Hear me, Poseidon, lord of the sea! If I am truly your son, grant that Odysseus, conqueror of Troy, son of Laertes of Ithaca, may never reach his home again. Or if he ever does reach Ithaca, may he have a long, miserable journey in another man's ship, may he lose all his companions, and may he find only confusion at his home!"

As he uttered this prayer, the Cyclops flung another huge boulder. This time the wave drove the ship towards its destination on the island where the other ships were waiting. Odysseus then sacrificed the great ram as a burnt offering to Zeus, but at the request of Poseidon, the king of the gods rejected the sacrifice and laid plans to destroy the ships and the trusty companions of Odysseus.

AEOLUS

THE next stop was the floating island of Aeolia, home of Aeolus, ruler of the winds. Aeolus gave Odysseus an ox-skin bag containing winds to blow him home, but the crew, thinking they had found a store of wine, released the blustering winds. The gale caught up the ships and whirled them far out to sea, and then back again to the isle of Aeolus.

THE HOSTILE GIANTS

SEVEN days later, they came to the land of the giant Laestrygonians, who threw great showers of huge stones down from the cliffs, smashing the ships and crushing the men. The giants speared the sailors like fish and carried them home for supper. Only the ship of Odysseus escaped; all the others were lost.

THE ENCHANTRESS

MOURNING their dead companions, the wanderers sailed on till they came to harbour on a rocky island. Odysseus climbed the cliff, from which he spied smoke rising from a grove of trees. He divided his company into two parties, putting one under the command of the fine warrior Eurylochus and taking charge of the other himself. Quickly they shook lots in a helmet, and out came the lot of Eurylochus, who started off to investigate with his twenty-two men.

In the grove they found a house built of polished stones and set in a clearing. All around the house prowled wolves and mountain lions. The band lost their terror when the beasts did not attack but leaped upon them like friendly dogs. These poor creatures later turned out to be really men that had been bewitched.

From the house came the voice of Circe, the beautiful enchantress, who sang as she worked at her loom. She was weaving a delicate gossamer fabric such as goddesses make.

Circe opened the shining doors and bade them all come in. Only the canny Eurylochus remained behind, for he suspected a trap. The sorceress seated her guests comfortably and served them a meal of cheese and meal and pale honey mixed with wine; but in the mixture she put a drug, to make them completely forget their native land. As soon as they had swallowed the brew, she tapped them with a wand, herded them into pens, and gave them beechnuts and acorns. Each man had turned instantly into a pig.

Now the dumbfounded Eurylochus rushed back to the ships and only finally found his tongue to tell his tale to the others.

Odysseus buckled on his great bronze sword, slung his bow on his shoulder, and told Eurylochus to show him the way; but Eurylochus pleaded with him to get away while he could with the men who were left.

"You remain here, Eurylochus; I am on my way." And Odysseus started off from the shore, up into the enchanted grove.

He was just about to enter when he met a handsome young man carrying a golden rod, who recognized him immediately. This was the messenger of the gods, Hermes.

"If you insist upon going, Odysseus, take this charm. Drop it in the brew she serves you, and it will keep you safe from harm."

Hermes gave him an herb which the gods call *moly*. It had a black root and a white flower.

Circe led Odysseus in, mixed him a brew, and dropped in her magic drug. When he drank it down, she tapped him with her wand, and cried, "Off to the sty with you!"

But he was not bewitched. He drew his sharp sword and leaped at the witch, intending to slay her; but she threw herself at his feet and blurted out in dismay, "Put up your sword! Surely you are Odysseus the hero—Hermes told me you would one day arrive from Troy. Let us be good friends!"

"I cannot trust you, when you have turned my companions into swine. Swear then to the gods that you will never harm me."

And Circe swore a solemn oath.

Then her four maids, who were nymphs of the springs and woods and sacred rivers, made preparations for welcoming the honoured guest. One covered the seats with linen and purple cloth. Another placed before them tables of silver with golden baskets on them. A third mixed delicious honey wine and set out cups of gold. The fourth heated water in a glittering copper cauldron.

Odysseus was led to a bath and Circe poured the warm soothing water over his head and shoulders till his weariness was no more. Then she rubbed his limbs with olive oil and gave him a rich tunic and cloak to wear. She led him to a fine carved chair, set a footstool under his feet, and the handmaidens fed to him a sumptuous feast.

But Odysseus was sick at heart and would not touch a thing.

"If you wish me to eat and drink, let me see my friends before my eyes."

Then Circe took her wand, went to the sty, drove out the swine, and rubbed their backs with another drug which immediately transformed them once again into men. They were handsomer and even younger than before. Even the enchantress was touched by the happiness of the companions.

"You are invited to a banquet. Go to your ship and bring back the others that I may entertain you all."

They all came, even Eurylochus, who took some persuading. And there on the island of Circe they remained for a full year, with plenty to eat and good sweet wine to drink.

WHEN the four seasons came round again, the men were eager to be on their way, and Odysseus reminded Circe of her promise to help them return safely home to Ithaca.

"First you must make a journey to the kingdom of the dead," she answered. "You must enter the realm of Hades and his queen Persephone, and there ask directions from the blind Theban seer Teiresias, who will tell you how you may at last reach home."

Odysseus and his men were shattered. No one had ever travelled to Hades in a ship!

But Circe told them how to set their sails, and what sacrifices and prayers to offer in the grove of Persephone; then she sent them a sail-filling wind to speed them on their way.

At last they came to the stream of Oceanus, the very edge of the world, and the land of the Cimmerians, wrapped in mist and cloud.

They found the grove and made their offerings. Then the souls of the dead came crowding up from Erebus, young men and brides, old men who had suffered, and warriors clad in bloodstained armour, and among them the Theban Teiresias, who spoke:

"Your voyage will be hard and dangerous, Odysseus; Poseidon is furious with you because you blinded his son, Polyphemus. Nevertheless you may reach home safely, if when you come near to an island where the herds of the sun god graze, you sail on and do not harm them. But if you touch the sheep and cattle of Apollo, I foretell destruction for your ship and your crew. It will be a long time, Odysseus, before you reach Ithaca, and there you will have to rid your house of many bold suitors wooing your faithful wife."

Having uttered the prophecy, the soul of Teiresias returned to the house of Hades. Then Odysseus questioned other ghosts of the dead as they drifted by: first his mother, then the wives and daughters of great men, and later the heroes who fell before the walls of Troy, Achilles among them. He told Achilles of the valour of his son Neoptolemus. Then he saw the thirsty Tantalus standing in a lake up to his chin. Whenever the old man who had challenged the gods bent his head to drink, the waters were sucked away. Fruit—pears, pomegranates, apples, figs, and ripe olives—hung from branches over his head; but when he reached for the food, the wind tossed it away.

He saw, too, the sweating Sisyphus, who suffered eternal punishment for betraying a secret of Zeus. Sisyphus spent the ages at the tedious task of rolling a monstrous stone up a great hill. Each time he neared the top, the weight proved too much and down the stone came to the bottom.

Finally the hosts of the dead set up a deafening cry, and Odysseus, fearful that Persephone might let lose some dreadful monster upon him, withdrew to the ship.

THE SIRENS

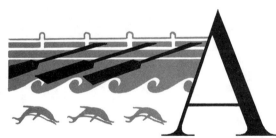

AS the ship left the river Oceanus and entered the open sea, a following breeze sped them on their way. Soon they were to reach the first of the dangers Circe had predicted: the isle of the Sirens, whose songs bewitched all men. Any man who came within earshot of their melodious voices never saw home again. There they sat in a bone-strewn meadow, surrounded by the remains of those they had lured to destruction. It was there that the wind died down and the ship was becalmed.

As the crew stowed the sail and took to the oars, Odysseus set to work kneading a large lump of wax which he chopped up into pellets. These he stuffed into the ears of all his men, one after another. Then he had the crew bind him hand and foot and tie him to the mast. Only in this way, Circe had told him, might he hear the Sirens' song.

As the ship drew near, the Sirens saw it and sent over the waves a melody of enchantment. The sweet, liquid sounds filled Odysseus with such a longing to hear more that he ordered his men to free him. He even pleaded with them; but his shouts and cries fell on deaf ears. They could not hear him any more than they could hear the Sirens' song, and disregarding his struggles and writhings, they firmly continued rowing, and the ship sped over the sea, safely out of earshot. Only then did they take the wax from their ears and release their commander from the mast.

IN HISTORY

What were the Sirens? Readers have been asking for generations.

Most scholars assume that the story, like the others in the *Odyssey*, is based on reality. Some identify the Sirens with the women of cannibal tribes, who lured sailors ashore so that they could be captured easily by the menfolk. Others believe that the Sirens were actually birds, whose appearance in the distance resembled women. Ships attempting to come close to rocky islands where such birds perched might be wrecked upon sharp rocks just under the water's surface.

In some stories the Sirens resembled birds, with wings given them by Demeter to search for Persephone but later made useless by the Muses. These stories are reminiscent of the Harpies, bird-winged creatures who troubled Aeneas and other voyagers, and who are considered to represent the sudden snatching away of a sailor by the sea.

T HE Sirens' isle safely bypassed, Odysseus sighted clouds of steam and a great rolling wave. The men became terrified at the roar of the sea, although they had not been told of the perils that Circe had described to their commander.

"Take heed and hold tight to the helm! Keep away from the steam, and hug the high cliff!" cried Odysseus.

They were passing through a strait so narrow you could shoot an arrow across. On one side, a cliff smooth and sheer rose straight up into the clouds. In its face gaped a gloomy cave, the home of Scylla, a ghastly monster with six enormously long necks. Each of its six voracious heads could pluck a victim from any passing ship.

The other cliff was lower, but to come close to it would mean total destruction. It was there the dreaded Charybdis lived, sucking down the water in a black whirlpool three times a day, and three times spewing it forth.

Every man was pale with fear as the helmsman just managed to keep the ship from being swallowed into the swirling depths, and no one even looked towards Scylla's lair. It was then the hungry heads snaked forth and snatched six of the crew, and swung them, gasping, into the cave. There Scylla devoured them.

APOLLO'S CATTLE

ADDENED by the horrible fate of their comrades, the adventurers sighted a delightful island where grazed the cattle that belonged to Apollo, god of the sun. The warning of the blind prophet Teiresias still echoed in the ears of Odysseus as he ordered the men to sail on.

The crew were weary, and Eurylochus spoke up for them.

"You must be made of iron, Odysseus. Let us go ashore and have a good meal; we can spend the night on the beach and set sail in the morning!"

When Odysseus at last gave in to their pleadings, it was against his better judgment, for he knew the gods were planning more troubles for him. He made every man swear a solemn oath not to touch a single head of cattle.

During the night, however, the cloud-gatherer Zeus sent the furious tempest, and in the morning Odysseus knew they were trapped, for the winds continued to blow. As the days went on, their stocks of grain and wine ran low. Hunger began to gnaw at the men, and as they roamed the island in search of game and fish they grumbled among themselves.

"It is foolish to die of starvation, surrounded as we are by food," said Eurylochus, when Odysseus was some distance away offering prayers to the gods. "Let us sacrifice the best of the cattle to Apollo, and we will build him a fine temple when we get home to Ithaca."

When Odysseus returned to the seashore, he smelled the delicious odour of sizzling fat. Hides lay strewn about, and roast beef crackled on the spit. He knew the fate they must meet, and he groaned aloud.

On the seventh day the tempest ceased and they set sail. No sooner were they out of sight of land than a black cloud appeared above the ship and the west wind struck with hurricane force. The mast snapped in two and the rigging came tumbling all over the deck.

Then Zeus launched his thunderbolt, and the ship reeled, struck by the lightning. The doomed men bobbed on the waves like so many gulls. There would be no homecoming for them.

Somehow Odysseus managed to lash two timbers together with an oxhide thong, and to these he clung. He drifted helplessly for nine days until, more dead than alive, he was washed up on the isle of Ogygia, where dwelt Calypso.

FROM CALYPSO'S ISLE

GREATLY concerned that the noble Odysseus sat, wretched and miserable, a prisoner on the isle of Calypso, Pallas Athene appealed to Zeus, who dispatched Hermes to the great cave of the radiant nymph.

There she sat, singing at her loom, her beautiful hair flowing over her shoulders as she thrust the golden shuttle to and fro.

"I rescued this man from the perilous sea," she said. "All his crew were drowned and his ship was smashed to pieces. I loved him and cherished him, and I wished to make him immortal like myself; but since no god can thwart the will of almighty Zeus, I'll let him go. I cannot give him a ship, but I will help him."

Then Hermes departed satisfied, and Calypso found the despondent Odysseus on the shore. Although he had at first been enchanted by the nymph, he no longer loved her, and spent each day staring out at the barren sea.

"Poor unhappy hero," she said. "I shall send you off at once. Build

133

yourself a raft, and I will stock it with bread and water and red wine. I will give you plenty of clothing and send a fair wind to bring you safely home."

At first Odysseus could not believe these words, but Calypso swore the most solemn oath by heaven and by earth and by the River Styx that she would work no mischief against him.

The following day, when dawn's rosy fingers parted the mists, Odysseus set to work with axe and adze in a grove of alder and aspen and tall pine. Twenty trees he felled. He made holes with a boring tool Calypso gave him and he fixed fast the deck planks with pegs. A mast he made, a yardarm and a steering oar, and the nymph brought him cloth for a sail. He dragged the craft to the sea on rollers.

On the morning of the fifth day Calypso saw him off, and for seventeen days he sailed guided by the stars. He was just approaching the land of the Phaeacians when Poseidon spied him, and could not resist one last blow.

He gathered the clouds, stirred up the deep with his trident, and set Night rushing down. Sail and yard were ripped from the raft and the timbers were scattered like chaff. Odysseus cried out, "How lucky were they who perished before the walls of Troy! At least they had funeral rites and proper burial—" and then he was snatched into the depths of the sea.

It was only through the pity of beautiful Ino, the foam-white sea goddess, and of Pallas Athene, that Odysseus was saved. Finally, battered and swollen, he was swept into the mouth of a river, where he lay among the reeds, overcome by a great weariness. He just managed to crawl to the bank, where he kissed the earth in gratitude.

AUSICAÄ, the lovely daughter of the Phaeacian king, awoke one morning from a pleasant dream. She had a vague recollection of a bridegroom coming, and of the lovely garments needed for a wedding. On a strange impulse, she asked her father to have the mules yoked to a cart, on which she heaped her best clothes, and away she went with her young maids to the river to launder the garments.

When the clothes were bright and spotless and spread out on the pebbled beach to dry, the young girls bathed and rubbed themselves with olive oil. Then they ate their meal, and started to play ball. It was then that Athene decided that Odysseus should be awakened by their merry squeals.

The maids were terrified when they saw the grimy man, who gave them one startled look and tried to cover himself with a fistful of reeds, and they scampered away. But Nausicaä stood her ground. Odysseus almost mistook her for Artemis, so tall and fair was she.

"If you are mortal, your parents are fortunate indeed, for I have never seen such beauty. Your bridegroom will be a very lucky man."

And he asked the princess to take pity on him, to give him clothes, and to please direct him to town.

"Stranger," she said, realizing that Odysseus was not a bad man, "you are in the land of the Phaeacians, and I am the daughter of their king, Alcinous. You shall not lack for clothes or anything else a wanderer may have for the asking."

She called to her maids to bring garments, and food and drink for the stranger. Then she told him he could follow along behind the cart with her maids, but before they reached the city he must let them go on ahead, in order to avoid gossip. He was to allow them enough time to reach the palace before entering the city himself.

"Then ask for the royal mansion, and walk through the courtyard to the great hall. There you shall see my mother sitting at the hearth, twisting yarn of deep purple by the light of the fire. Pass by my father's throne and lay your hands in my mother's lap. If she is pleased with you she will persuade my father to speed you safely home."

With a crack of the whip, the princess departed, leaving Odysseus to follow her instructions. And Athene wrapped him in a mist so that he would not be seen going through the town and entering the palace.

It was only when he entered the great hall and fell before the Queen that the mist faded away, and all grew silent throughout the hall.

"Queen Arete, I come as a suppliant to you and your lord," he said. "May the gods grant you happiness if you send me home without delay, for I have long suffered hardships far from my friends."

Thereupon the queen's husband took the castaway by the hand and led him from the hearth to the seat of honour which his favourite son vacated. A handmaid poured water from a golden pitcher into a silver bowl that Odysseus might wash his hands. A table was laid for him, at which he ate and drank. Then the king ordered wine for the whole company, so that all could make a libation to Zeus, the god of wanderers.

It was only then that the queen, who had recognized the tunic and cloak he wore since she had made them herself, came straight to the point and asked, "Now, my guest, who are you, and where, may I ask, did you get those clothes?"

And Odysseus, son of Laertes of mountainous Ithaca, began his long story to the spellbound Phaeacians.

THE HOMECOMING

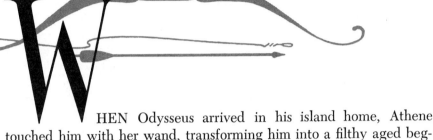

WHEN Odysseus arrived in his island home, Athene touched him with her wand, transforming him into a filthy aged beggar, and even his faithful old swineherd did not recognize him. However, the swineherd welcomed the stranger to his cabin and told him of the suitors who for years had been eating up the wealth of the absent master, who would never return. The swaggering wooers had installed themselves in his palace while they paid suit to Odysseus' wife, Penelope.

The fair Penelope, who was weaving a great shroud for noble old Laertes, still dreamed of her husband's return. For years she delayed making a choice among the suitors by asking them all to wait until the shroud was finished. Each night she would unravel the work she had done by day.

When Odysseus' son, Telemachus, came to the swineherd's cabin, he did not recognize his father. Then Athene appeared to Odysseus in the form of a fine, tall woman, but she was not seen by Telemachus, for the gods do not show themselves to everyone. Athene once more touched Odysseus with her golden wand, transforming him into a rugged man, very much younger, tanned dark and bearded, and she clothed him in fine raiment.

Telemachus mistook him for one of the gods.

"Why do you rank me with the immortals? I am no god," Odysseus replied. "I am your father for whom you have so long mourned and put up with the wrongdoings of men."

Telemachus could not believe his ears and eyes. When Odysseus convinced him, the young man embraced his noble father and burst into tears. Then Odysseus told his son the long tale of his sufferings and wanderings during the past twenty years.

Finally the two plotted to rid the palace of the hundred and more suitors.

"We have Athene and Zeus to help us," Odysseus confided to his son.

Once again clad in rags, a tattered sack slung on his shoulders, and accompanied by the swineherd, Odysseus arrived at the entrance of the guest house. As they were talking, a mangy old hound lying at the gate lifted his head and pricked his ears. This was Odysseus' old hunting dog, Argus, whom he had bred and trained. At the sound of his master's voice, Argus dropped his ears and wagged his tail, but he could not move to go to him. There he lay, old and vermin-ridden. Odysseus saw him, and secretly wiped a tear from his eye. Then the old dog died, having lived to see his master once more after twenty years of waiting.

The suitors had been amusing themselves at games and contests in the courtyard, but when dinner was ready they swarmed into the hall like locusts. Some of them pitied the ragged beggar and gave him food, but the overbearing Antinous struck him with a footstool. At last, when the suitors had left for the night, Odysseus sat at the feet of Penelope, who confided to the stranger:

"If Odysseus does not soon return, I will hold an archery contest among the suitors, and the winner I will marry."

The following morning she appeared before them all accompanied by an attendant carrying the master's bow, a quiver full of arrows, and the dozen ax-heads she intended to use in the contest.

"Hear me, you who have been wooing me year in and year out as an excuse for eating and drinking. This is the great bow of Odysseus. Whoever can string it and then shoot an arrow through the openings of twelve ax-heads set in a line shall become my husband."

Then Telemachus set up the axes, stamping down the earth to hold them. He took the first try, and could not even bend the bow. Another tried and likewise failed. Then the suitors set to work, warming it before the fire and greasing it with lard. Each one took his turn, and each one failed to bend it.

They were about to abandon the contest, when up spoke the ragged Odysseus:

"I beg you, let me try the bow to see if my arms are as strong as they used to be, after all my wanderings and hardships."

The suitors scoffed at him, though they were really afraid that he might by some chance succeed. However, both Telemachus and Penelope put in a word for the stranger and the bow was placed in the hands of Odysseus.

Odysseus examined it carefully and balanced it in his hand. Then, as easily as a skilled musician stretches a new string on his harp, he strung the great bow and twanged the string. The suitors were dumbfounded and grew pale. From overhead came a clap of thunder, a good omen from Zeus.

Odysseus picked up the arrow from the table before him, fitted it to the bow and, still sitting on his chair, drew back the string, took aim and let fly. He did not miss. Straight through the twelve ax-heads sped the shaft, and clean out the other end.

"Come, Telemachus. Let us entertain our guests while there is still daylight," said Odysseus.

Telemachus slung on his sword, grasped his spear, and sprang to his father's side, fully armed. Odysseus stripped off his rags and spread the arrows at his feet.

"Your game is over at last," he cried, "and now for another target!"

He let fly straight at Antinous, who was holding a golden goblet in both his hands. The arrow struck him in the throat. Blood spurted from his nostrils.

The hall was in an uproar as the chief of the suitors fell. Wildly the others scanned the wall for weapons, but not a shield nor spear could be seen.

"Dogs!" shouted Odysseus. "You thought I would never return from Troy. You have been wasting my wealth, wooing my wife, and using my household as you wished. And you have not feared the gods who rule the broad heavens. Now you shall die!"

Pale fear descended on them. Only one, Eurymachus, could find his tongue: "There lies the guilty man—Antinous. Spare the rest of us, Odysseus, and we will make good your loss!"

"Eurymachus, even if you gave me all your estates I would not stay my hand from slaying every single one of you. Fight, I say! Or flee if you can!"

But Eurymachus cried, "Turn up the tables! Draw your swords, my friends!"

He leaped towards Odysseus, but at that instant the hero let fly another arrow, which caught him in the chest, and he went sprawling over a table, scattering victuals and goblets to the floor. Telemachus struck down another with a spear as he ran upon them. Then he raced to the armoury for more shields, helmets, and spears for himself and his father, and for their two trusty servants, the swineherd and a drover.

When he returned, one suitor lay dead for each of Odysseus' arrows. Then the four set upon the suitors with sword and spear. The floor ran blood.

Finally all the suitors were dead; only the minstrel and the herald were spared. And Odysseus sent his old nurse to tell Penelope that her husband Odysseus, son of Laertes of Ithaca, was home.

IN HISTORY

Although the *Odyssey* claims to be Odysseus' tale of his travels, it is unlikely that it is actually a record of any single voyage. The researches of scholars have succeeded in identifying many of the lands visited in the *Odyssey* and, although there is considerable disagreement, it is plain that they were scattered about the whole known world of the time.

The travels of Odysseus seem to range over the whole Mediterranean and into the north Atlantic. After leaving Troy, he apparently went north to Ismaros, on the northern coast of the Aegean. Then he turned south, sailed through the Aegean and around the southerly tip of the Peloponnese (Cape Malea), attempting to turn north again to Ithaca. Instead, however, he was blown over to Africa and landed on the coast of Libya, the land of the Lotus-Eaters. Other ancient writers, too, speak of Libyan tribes who often ate a sweet mixture of fruit and grain.

Odysseus tried to get north from Africa, but ended up far west of Greece at the Cyclops' island. This is usually identified with Sicily. From there he went to the floating isle of Aeolus, and then to the land of the Laestrygonians—probably either the north-west coast of Sicily or the west of Italy.

There is good reason for the speculation that the story of the disaster which befell the ships at the hands of the Laestrygonians records a well-founded fear held by Greek mariners. Various locations around the west coast of Italy have produced piles of human bones, split so that the marrow could be drawn out. Such bones are clear evidence of cannibals. One theory even identifies the Sirens whom Odysseus later escaped as part of the same story, for it is possible that women were used to attract the crews of passing ships to the shore where the men were hidden, waiting to attack and kill.

Odysseus went next to the isle where Circe lived, probably another island in the same area of the Tyrrhenian Sea. Doubtless Greek sailors had seen large numbers of swine on the island, and concluded that they were transformed sailors, who perhaps had landed and never returned to their ships.

Circe sent Odysseus to the land of the Cimmerians, the fog-shrouded land at the end of the earth. There seems to be little doubt that this tale recounts the vague and fearful memories of mariners who had ventured beyond the Pillars of Hercules and sailed up the coast of western Europe. The northern lands would seem so far from Greece, the climate and vegetation so strange, that sailors might well believe they had come to the ends of the earth and the entrance to the lands of the dead. Other legends also suggest that occasionally a Greek ship roamed far to the north; for example, Jason and the Argonauts barely escaped being crushed by the Clashing Rocks, which seem to be icebergs.

The next episode finds Odysseus again near Italy and Sicily, passing the Sirens' isle and passing between Scylla and Charybdis—generally identified with the

Straits of Messina. Along the coast of Italy there are many spots where the action of the sea causes strange noises. There are roaring sounds, as if great herds of cattle are drinking; there are hissing sounds that might be made by great snakes; from some of these places, as a wave rises, jets of compressed air mixed with water are shot out. These are the grottoes which dot parts of the coastline.

The rest of the adventures probably took place in the Adriatic, and sound as if the ship had gone far to the north before turning south for Ithaca. The home of Nausicaä is assumed by some to be Corfu, an island lying off the modern border between Albania and Greece, and less than a hundred miles from Ithaca.

The Odyssey, then, probably embodies dozens of sailors' tales of far, mysterious lands, exaggerated in retelling but bearing within them echoes of remembered truth.

ECHOES IN LITERATURE

The elements of the story of Odysseus have been turned to interesting use in two works bearing as title his Roman name, Ulysses.

The older of the two is a poem by the Victorian poet Tennyson, a dramatic monologue in which the aging Ulysses, idle and restless at home in Ithaca after his adventures, decides to set out on the sea once more. Tennyson shows the hero longing for new experience, determined not to grow useless and rusty, but always

To strive, to seek, to find, and not to yield.

The second Ulysses is a long novel by the modern Irish writer James Joyce. Joyce's Ulysses is not the hero of legend, but a counterpart who, during one day in modern Dublin, encounters a series of incidents which are to some extent parallel to the adventures of Odysseus, even though they belong to their own time and place.

THE AENEID

The Aeneid is not, strictly speaking, part of mythology, for it was composed in frank imitation of the *Odyssey* by a Roman poet for a specific purpose.

Publius Vergilius Maro (70-19 B.C.) was one of the most honoured writers during the period when Augustus was emperor of Rome. At that time, educated Romans believed that the Greeks had reached the pinnacle of culture, and looked to them for models for their writing. Virgil, as he is known to English-speaking people, was no exception. He studied Greek poetry, and imitated the Greek masters so well that he surpassed most of them—a feat not surprising when we remember how much the Romans had advanced in many fields.

Eventually Virgil undertook the task of writing his city's national epic, for he wished that Rome had something similar to the Greek *Iliad* and *Odyssey*. His aim was not only to account for the origin of the Roman people, but also to instil in them a deep pride in their city and their heritage. The result was the *Aeneid*, which was left completed only in draft form, unpolished and unrevised, at his death. It was published just as Virgil left it, yet remains one of the truly tremendous literary creations of the world.

Since it was natural for Virgil to turn for inspiration to the epics he so much admired, the works of Homer are the basis for his epic. However, he told his tale from the point of view of Aeneas, the Trojan hero; in the *Aeneid*, the Greeks are villains, not heroes.

In recounting the fate-tossed wanderings of his hero, Virgil relied heavily on the stories of the wanderings of Odysseus. However, a comparison of the two can be made only as regards the stories, for in style and feeling they are as different as works can be. No one condemns Virgil for using old material; they praise him for the creation of a moving national epic.

Virgil naturally used the Latin names for gods and goddesses. To him Zeus was Jupiter, Hera was Juno, and Hermes, Mercury. Aphrodite, mother of Aeneas, was Venus.

THE SACK OF TROY

WHILE the Greeks, having gained entry to the city by the stratagem of the wooden horse, were hacking their bloody way through the streets of Troy, the ghost of dead Hector appeared to Aeneas.

In his dream, Aeneas was horrified at the appearance of his lost friend, for Hector was black with blood-caked dust, his feet swollen where the thongs had pierced them, and his whole body a mass of open wounds. Hector did not answer Aeneas' frenzied questions, but told him in simple terms what was happening in the rest of the city.

"Troy is taken," he said with a deep sigh. "There is no point in fighting any more, for if valour could have saved the city, I myself would have done it.

"To you, Troy entrusts her omens and her household gods. Take them, and bear them to a new home—" and snatching the sacred fire which burned nearby, the dead Hector handed it to Aeneas.

He disappeared, and the sleeper was wakened by a tumult growing in the streets; anguished wails and shrieks of fear mingled with the clash of weapons. Aeneas rushed to look, and stood transfixed by the horrible scene below. He realized that Hector's words were true. Troy had fallen.

For a few moments he attempted to fight, then realized how hopeless was the task, for all before him was spread a scene of total desolation. Men and women lay dead everywhere, and victorious Greeks shouted rejoicing over the bodies which clogged the streets. The paths and gutters were flowing with blood. Even the palace, surely the strongest place in the city, had fallen, and old Priam himself, after seeing his sons cut down before his eyes, had been brutally slaughtered on the altar by Neoptolemus, son of Achilles.

To Aeneas, the only course open was that advised by Hector—to flee from the ravaged city. Quickly he gathered together his wife and his son, little Ascanius, or Iulus, and on his strong shoulders placed his aged and crippled father, Anchises.

As the little band made its way through the streets, carrying the sacred emblems of fallen Troy, the first of many tragic events took place. Looking over his shoulder to make sure that the whole family was still together, Aeneas could not find his wife, Creusa. He shouted for her, but received no answer amid the din and tumult. With aching heart, he knew that there was no time to return and look. He never saw Creusa again.

Many refugee Trojans joined Aeneas in his flight from Troy. Their voyage was perilous, for they were at the mercy not only of sea and wind, but also of the gods. Aeneas had a powerful ally in his mother, Venus; however, Juno had an implacable hatred for all Trojans since her slight by Paris, and she reserved a special wrath for Aeneas, leader of the only surviving band.

DIDO

ENEAS and his companions were bound for Italy, where it was destined that they should found a new city, a second Troy to surpass even the first in glory. Juno hated to see this come about, partly because of her loathing of the Trojan race, and partly because a new city in the west would be a rival to her beloved Carthage.

Carthage had been founded by a woman, Dido, who had led a small band there after she had been driven from her own land by a murderous brother. She was young and lovely, and a widow; Juno therefore evolved the plan of keeping Aeneas from ever reaching Italy by having him fall in love with Dido, who would persuade him to remain with her in Africa.

However, when Venus realized the fate for which her son was heading, she began to worry that he would lose the greatness which had been destined for him. Seeking the counsel of Jupiter, she begged him to remember the promises he had made. Smiling at her concern, Jupiter dried the goddess' tears and told her she need not worry; her son would not stay in Carthage forever.

With this assurance, Venus did not oppose a romance between Dido and Aeneas, for she could be assured of her son's safety if he were favoured by the queen. And with the approval of the goddess of love, no sooner did Aeneas and Dido lay eyes on each other than their hearts were moved.

For many months Aeneas lingered by the side of Dido, who received all the Trojan band with warmth and treated Aeneas to the courtesies belonging to a king. Living in luxury, deeply in love with Dido, he forgot the plans he had made to sail on to Italy. For a while the two lovers lived an idyllic existence which rivalled paradise.

Eventually, however, Jupiter remembered his promise to Venus. He sent Mercury to visit Aeneas.

"How long are you going to stay here, forgetting your duty?" the god demanded. Startled, Aeneas could only cast his eyes downward.

"I have been sent to you by Jupiter himself, the king of heaven," Mercury continued, fixing Aeneas with an accusing stare. "He bids you leave this place and seek the kingdom which is your destiny!"

With that he flew off, leaving Aeneas aware that he must carry out the god's orders and leave Carthage and his beloved Dido. But how, he wondered, could he break the news to her?

His heart full of grief, Aeneas decided to take the easy course. He would depart that very night, in secret, so that he would not have to see the anguish in Dido's eyes when she learned of his leavetaking.

Nevertheless, the queen found out what was about to happen. She could not believe that her beloved meant to steal away from her, and gently pleaded with him to stay.

Steeling his heart against her pleas, Aeneas answered simply that

Jupiter had ordered him to go, that he was not married to Dido and thus had no obligation to her, and that nothing could induce him to transgress the commands of the god.

"False traitor!" Dido screamed. "Will you deny that I found you, an outcast? That I took you in? That I let you share my home and made you partner in my reign? If all these mean nothing to you, then go!"

She turned away, fainting, and her maids bore her to her couch. Sick at heart, Aeneas left. Without further delay, he gathered his companions and sailed away from Carthage.

That night a red glow hung over the African city. It could be seen even from Aeneas' ships, but he did not know what it was.

Feeling herself forsaken by her lover and betrayed by heaven, Dido had ordered a tremendous funeral pyre built, had climbed it, and had plunged the abandoned sword of Aeneas into her breast.

ECHOES IN LITERATURE

Dido's story has provided ample material for poets, and her name is used often as a symbol of tragic passion. Chaucer, a fourteenth-century poet, told the story in his *Legende of Good Women*, and two centuries later Christopher Marlowe wrote a play entitled *The Tragedie of Dido*.

One of the best-known versions of the story has been a musical one, the seventeenth-century opera *Dido and Aeneas* by English composer Henry Purcell.

HEN his ship finally reached the west coast of Italy, Aeneas sought out the Sibyl of Cumae, a wise woman who lived in a cave and who could see into the future. Instead of telling Aeneas what lay before him, however, the Sibyl told him that she would lead him to the underworld to find his father Anchises, who had perished on the voyage, and Anchises would tell him what he needed to know.

The descent into the underworld was frightening. To mollify Cerberus, Aeneas had to imitate Psyche's trick of bribing him with cake. Once reached, the land of the dead proved awesome. On all sides Aeneas was pressed by dim ghosts, sometimes moaning horribly, sometimes screaming in anguish.

In one terrible part, called the Fields of Mourning, roamed the souls of unhappy lovers who had taken their own lives; there, wandering by herself, was Dido. Aeneas pleaded with her for some sign of recognition, some tale of her death, but in vain—she neither spoke nor looked at him. Deeply shaken by the sight of his beloved, Aeneas could scarcely go on.

Finally the travellers came to the Elysian Fields, where dwelt the souls of the blest. There they found Anchises, and happy was the reunion between father and son.

Anchises showed Aeneas the souls of his descendants, yet unborn, who would be the Romans of the future. The sight of this magnificent company lifted Aeneas' sad heart, and he listened carefully to Anchises' instructions about the founding of this great city.

THE WAR IN ITALY

Y the intervention of Juno, most of the Italian tribes opposed any settlement of Trojans in their land. However, Aeneas was received by Latinus, king of Latium, and so won his confidence that Latinus agreed to let the stranger marry his daughter, Lavinia. From their marriage, Latinus felt, would be born a race which would master not only Italy, but the whole world.

The marriage was opposed by Turnus, a neighbouring king who had hoped to marry Lavinia himself. Determined to drive out the Trojans, Turnus declared war on Latinus and his people. For a long time the war raged, until at last Turnus and Aeneas met in single combat. The king had no chance against Aeneas, son of the goddess Venus.

After the death of Turnus, there was no more opposition to the marriage of Aeneas and Lavinia, or to the settlement of Trojans on the banks of the Tiber. The descendants of Aeneas were the Romans, and he is considered the founder of the most powerful nation in the ancient world.

ECHOES IN ART

The epics, particularly those of Homer, have proved a rich source for artists.

One of the most famous paintings in the world is Rubens' *Judgment of Paris* (Dresden). It shows a rustic Paris, accompanied by a remarkably similar Hermes, being confronted by the three goddesses who, like all the females painted by Rubens, are extremely large and plump.

Proof that the epics were popular subjects for painting even in classical times is provided by the wall-paintings preserved for two thousand years in such places as Pompeii, a town buried by a volcanic eruption in 79 A.D. and still being un-earthed. One of the paintings there, for example, shows the sacrifice at Aulis, where Iphigeneia, arms raised in supplication, is being borne to the altar by two brawny soldiers.

One of the best-known images of Zeus is that seen in Ingres' painting repre-senting Thetis appealing to the king of the gods, in the Aix-en-Provence Museum. Bearded Zeus, sitting majestically upon his throne, is huge compared to the nymph who pleads with him.

Countless paintings have depicted some part of the Trojan war. El Greco's Laocoön group shows the serpent writhing about the bodies of the old man and the boys, though their forms are less contorted than those shown in a·famous ancient marble carving of the group. A touching painting is David's *Hector*, show-ing the body of the hero languid and vulnerable after being stripped of its armour by Achilles.

Among the well-known paintings of Odysseus are a Turner (National Gallery, London), in which Odysseus shouts insults to Polyphemus from his little ship, and a Pintoricchio (National Gallery, London), showing the faithful Penelope at the loom, surrounded by suitors.

Circe has been a favourite of artists, and paintings show her surrounded by animals of various kinds, new forms of the sailors who fell under her spell.

PART FOUR

THE TRAGEDIES

GREEK TRAGEDY

Perhaps the greatest cultural heritage we claim from ancient Greece is **drama**, especially the kind we call **tragedy**.

The popularity of plays in this century makes it difficult for us to imagine a time when drama did not exist. Both comedy and tragedy originated in Greece before the sixth century B.C., and grew out of primitive religious ritual: comedy originated in festivals celebrating the fertility of the earth, and tragedy in rites honouring the god Dionysus.

The word *tragedy* is derived from the Greek *goat-song*, and we believe that its first form was the choral recitation which accompanied the ritual slaughter of a goat, an important part of the religious ceremony. The song usually dealt with mythological material, particularly the events associated with Dionysus.

Later, true tragic drama was evolved in Athens. Tradition states that a poet named Thespis instituted the practice of having one person stand apart from the chorus at certain times to deliver a dramatic recitation. Sometimes he gave a monologue, in which he alone spoke; sometimes he entered into a dialogue with the chorus. Thespis' new form of choral presentation became so popular in Athens that it was adopted as a major part of the festivals of Dionysus.

Important changes were made by two poets who wrote about a century later than Thespis. Aeschylus, the earliest of the great tragedians, introduced a second actor to stand apart from the chorus, which meant that either actor could speak alone, either could talk with the chorus, or both could act together in a dramatic scene, with the chorus commenting to the audience upon the action. Sophocles increased the number to three, and later as many as four actors could appear in a tragedy.

All tragedies were presented in Athens on one of two occasions. A few were seen during the *Lenaea*, or Festival of the Winepress. Most, however, were presented at the *Greater Dionysia*. When there were no festivals at Athens, plays would sometimes be taken on the road, to travel from city to city.

Three contests were held at the Greater Dionysia: one for comedy, one for *dithyramb*, or choral ode, and one for tragedy. The final three days of the festival were devoted to a contest between three tragic poets, each of whom had a whole day in which to present a group of three tragedies, on one theme or different subjects, and a lighter work to conclude. The plays were presented in a *theatron*, a huge semicircle of seats raised above a central *orchestra*, a flat circular area in which the actors performed. The theatre at Athens held about 17,000, and probably was filled for many festival performances. Athenians were at first admitted free, and later, when they were required to pay admission, the amount was refunded by the state to anyone who claimed need. Some scholars believe that Athenians were even paid a sum of money to compensate them for the days spent at the theatre. The state also paid several actors to perform in each presentation.

Many poets wrote tragedy, but the works of only three great ones have survived.

The first great tragedian was Aeschylus, who lived from 525 to 455 B.C. and first won the dramatic contest in 484. He apparently believed that his greatest distinction was that he had fought for his land at Marathon, for this is what is mentioned on his tombstone; however, he achieved lasting glory through the seven plays that survive from the ninety or so that he wrote. His primary interest as a playwright was in the ways of the gods, and his characters lack real depth.

Aeschylus was followed by Sophocles (496-406 B.C.), considered by many to be the greatest of the Greek tragedians. He was more interested than his predecessor in mankind, and his plays assert both eternal laws of heaven and the worth and dignity of man. Among the hundred and twenty-five plays which we think Sophocles must have written, only seven still exist, but among them are Oedipus the King and Antigone, both considered creations of genius.

The third great playwright was Euripides (c.485-405 B.C.), whose thought probably reflects changing religious feelings of his time, for a strong note of scepticism runs through his work. Euripides was not particularly interested in the actions of the gods, but preferred to concentrate upon human beings. His plays contain penetrating psychological studies of the feelings and motives of his characters.

Most plays followed the same structural pattern. The typical tragedy opened with a prologue, by which the author gave necessary information to his audience. This was followed by the appearance of the chorus, singing and dancing; they remained on stage throughout the play, though later in the fifth century their importance decreased. Then the actors appeared, and the rest of the play would be presented through alternate appearances of actors and chorus. The actors were always male, and sometimes wore huge masks to suggest the part they played. They also wore high-heeled boots to give them greater height.

The most profound explanation of Greek tragedy is contained in the Poetics of Aristotle.

Aristotle explained that the purpose of tragedy was the **catharsis**, or the purging of the emotions through the combination of pity and terror. The action, he said, was elevated above the normal level of human life, and the language in which the events were related or presented was to be lofty and dignified. The central figure was the tragic hero, and the play recounted a change in his fortunes; he defined the tragic hero "as man who is highly renowned and prosperous, but one who is not pre-eminently virtuous and just, whose misfortune is brought upon him not by vice and depravity but by some error of judgment or frailty."

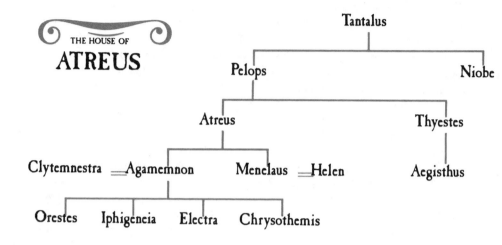

THE HOUSE OF

ATREUS

Tantalus

Pelops

Niobe

Atreus

Thyestes

Clytemnestra ═ Agamemnon   Menelaus ═ Helen

Aegisthus

Orestes   Iphigeneia   Electra   Chrysothemis

The story of ill-fated Agamemnon and his family is told in a trilogy of plays called the *Oresteia*, written in the fifth century B.C. by Aeschylus.

The first play in sequence is *Agamemnon*, which tells the events which occurred when the great king arrived home from Troy. The second, *The Libation Bearers*, takes place ten years later, when Orestes returns to his mother's home, and ends with his pursuit by the Furies. The final play, *The Eumenides*, finishes the story.

Sophocles and Euripides, the other great tragedians of Greece, each told the story of Orestes' revenge in drama. Both their plays are entitled *Electra*.

An extension of the story was made by Euripides, who, in *Iphigeneia in Tauris*, recounted the reunion of Orestes with his long-vanished sister, Iphigeneia.

MORTAL named Tantalus had received great honour from the gods, so much, in fact, that some people claimed he must be the son of Zeus himself. However, he himself admitted to being a mere human.

But Tantalus had a conceit greater, perhaps, than that possessed even by the gods. He may have been impressed the first time he was invited to share the gods' repast of nectar and ambrosia on Mount Olympus, feasts to which no other mortal had even dreamed of being invited, but the excitement soon wore off, and Tantalus believed himself not only the equal of the gods, but far smarter and more perceptive than they were.

He first repudiated the gods' hospitality by stealing some of the heavenly food under his cloak, and laughingly offering it to his friends. The gods did not even know that he had tricked them, he claimed; what was more, he had a scheme which would deceive them even further and reveal their dullness.

The means which Tantalus chose to expose what he believed to be the ignorance of the gods was grotesque almost beyond belief. He nonchalantly murdered his son Pelops, cut the body into pieces, and added them to a stew which he had prepared for the gods, for he had even become so bold as to invite them to eat at his house.

The deception did not succeed. The gods drew back in horror from the meal, all except Demeter who, her attention distracted, ate some meat which turned out to have been part of Pelops' left shoulder.

For his conceit and his lack of respect for the gods, and for his crime, Tantalus was subjected to a cruel death at the hands of the gods, and was made to suffer eternal torture in the land of the damned: he was consumed by pangs of hunger and raging thirst, while cool lake waters and succulent fruit remained always just beyond his reach.

Pelops was restored to life and his shoulder replaced by a piece of ivory; he lived a long and happy life. He was almost the only one of Tantalus' descendants to do so, for, besides drawing eternal punishment upon himself, the conceited mortal had drawn the gods' curse on his line for all time.

One of the first to suffer was Tantalus' daughter, Niobe. She married Amphion, the regent of Thebes, and bore him seven sons and seven daughters. As they grew up, handsome and strong, Niobe began to be filled with such pride that she made a foolish boast: "I have fourteen fine children; I should be worshipped instead of Leto, who has only two!"

Leto, whose children were Apollo and Artemis, summoned them to her side. Angry at the insult to his mother, Apollo drew his bow and slew the seven sons of Niobe; anguished at their loss, she still claimed her seven daughters made her greater than Leto. Thereupon Artemis drew her bow, and soon the daughters of Niobe lay in the dust. Maddened by sorrow, their father took his own life.

Her family all dead through her own unbridled pride, Niobe could not stop her tears from flowing. She was changed into a great rock, from which rivulets of tears continually flow.

Pelops' two most famous children were Atreus and Thyestes. They were close in age, and became rivals for the kingship of Mycenae, a position which was eventually won by Atreus.

Their rivalry extended into other areas as well, and Thyestes soon was discovered to have seduced the wife of his brother. Furious, Atreus pretended to be ignorant of the whole affair, and invited his brother to dine with him.

Thyestes ate a hearty meal of meat, enjoying his brother's friendliness for the first time in years, and thankful that his relationship with his sister-in-law had evidently escaped detection. When the meal was finished and Thyestes leaned back, satiated, Atreus bade a servant bring in the platters bearing the rest of what they had eaten.

On the platters lay the bloody remains of Thyestes' own sons.

The father fell back, vomiting, and in his maddened horror pronounced a curse on the house of Atreus.

Atreus too had two sons, Agamemnon and Menelaus. Both became great kings, Menelaus of Sparta, and Agamemnon of most of Greece, for he drew tribute from Mycenae, Corinth, and a dozen other cities. Between them, the brothers were the wealthiest and most powerful lords of Greece. The brothers married sisters, one of whom was already famed throughout the world; Helen, daughter of Leda and perhaps of Zeus, married Menelaus and lived with him until Paris of Troy stole her away. Agamemnon married Clytemnestra, no match for her sister in beauty, but a regal and intelligent woman. The beginnings of their union were not auspicious, for Clytemnestra had been forced to marry Agamemnon after he had killed her husband.

Nor was the death of her first husband the only grudge which Clytemnestra held against Agamemnon. He had, some said, dashed to death her infant at the same time he killed her husband. More horrible, he had sacrificed the daughter which Clytemnestra had borne to him.

This deed took place at Aulis, where the Greek fleet was assembled prior to sailing for Troy. A great calm had beset them, and an oracle had warned that no wind would rise until Agamemnon sent for his daughter, Iphigeneia, and offered her as a sacrifice to propitiate the gods. The king may have been loath to do so, but he overcame his natural disgust and sent a message to Clytemnestra to send the girl, pretending that she was to be married to one of the heroes setting out for Troy. Iphigeneia arrived, dressed in wedding finery, and Agamemnon had the unnatural deed carried out.

157

When Agamemnon was away at Troy, Clytemnestra took as her lover another man, Aegisthus. By the design of the gods, Aegisthus was the son of Thyestes, born after the dreadful banquet. His role was to be the avenger of his father, long since dead, on the house of Atreus.

Agamemnon returned in triumph from the wars, to be met at his door by his wife, her head high, offering him affectionate and humble words of welcome. All the assembled crowd knew that Clytemnestra had been living, for years, in Agamemnon's own palace with her lover, and they were startled, and a little alarmed, by the warm welcome she gave her returning husband. Clytemnestra had even rolled out a carpet of purple for her husband to tread upon as he strode into the palace he had not entered for ten years.

The king, however, had not returned alone. With him rode the prize of all the Trojan captives, Cassandra, the prophetess whose curse was that she would never be believed.

The crowd surged around this strange beauty, left alone when Agamemnon entered his palace. They were filled with wonder when she chanted, in a peculiar, far-away voice, of long-past deeds and the smell of blood. Finally Cassandra leaped from the carriage and rushed into the palace.

Soon a scream of agony cut the air.

Clytemnestra slowly came out the palace door, facing the crowd. Her robe was spattered with blood. In a calm voice she told them that she and Aegisthus had killed Agamemnon and his woman captive.

"This was not a murder, this was an execution," Clytemnestra announced. She told the crowd of the crimes committed by her husband against her and her children.

Clytemnestra and Aegisthus ruled in place of Agamemnon, with the consent of their subjects. Their only fear was the children of Agamemnon, but the daughters, Electra and Chrysothemis, were married to lowly farmers, and the son, Orestes, was far away in another land.

Though the years passed, desire for revenge of her father's murder filled the heart of Electra. Her sister had bowed easily to the will of Aegisthus, but Electra was of stronger stuff, and revered her dead father's memory. She longed for the time when her brother would return to take vengeance.

Orestes, though he knew about the death of Agamemnon, was bewildered about what action he should take. On the one hand, he knew it was his duty to avenge the death of his father. This was a burden placed upon every son whose parent had died by foul means. But to do so would mean killing his mother, and matricide was loathed by the gods above all other crimes.

The young man in desperation consulted the oracle of Apollo at Delphi. He received instructions which could not be misunderstood: he must avenge the death of his father.

Orestes, still full of misgivings, travelled immediately to the court of his mother, accompanied by his closest friend and confidant. Once there, he was recognized immediately by Electra, who whispered that he had not come a moment too soon, for the crime was becoming heavier on their souls as each day passed.

Orestes entered the palace and killed Aegisthus almost immediately.

When Orestes came, bloody sword hanging at his side, to his mother, Clytemnestra tried one desperate measure to dissuade him. She bared her breast and reminded him of how she had borne him, had given him life, how he had nestled in her arms when he was a tiny infant.

Orestes' heart was filled with sorrow, but he had resolved that no emotion was going to woo him from his ordeal. He did not even look at his mother's pleading eyes.

"Come with me," he said, simply. And Clytemnestra went.

After his father's death had been fully avenged and the two murderers lay dead in Agamemnon's palace, Orestes turned to leave. His eyes widened in horror when he saw the grim figures awaiting him.

Outside the palace door stood three horrible hags, their eyes bloodshot and fiery, their hands holding whips. They were the Erinnyes, Orestes knew—the Furies who would hound him, scourging with their whips, until the day of his death. Even though his mother's death had been justified, he was to be punished for it as an unnatural deed.

The Furies pursued Orestes cruelly until his suffering came to the attention of Apollo.

"I told Orestes, when he came to my oracle at Delphi, what he must do," he said. "He therefore acted under my direction—the direction of a god. The Furies must cease their torment!"

Following the god's words, Orestes knew that he had carried out the final dreadful act of the curse. He would suffer no longer, but could walk free among men. The Furies were changed into the Eumenides, or Kindly Ones, and became beneficent powers in the world.

ECHOES IN LITERATURE

The story of the House of Atreus appears to have been one of the most important subjects of Greek tragedy, for no fewer than eight of the surviving works of the great tragedians are built upon the myth. These include Aeschylus' *Agamemnon, Libation Bearers,* and *Eumenides;* Sophocles' *Electra;* and Euripides' *Iphigeneia at Aulis, Iphigeneia in Taurus, Electra,* and *Orestes.* The subjects of most of these are clear from the titles. *Libation Bearers* is named from the chorus of Trojan women who offer libations at the tomb of Agamemnon, and treats of the killing of Clytemnestra and Aegisthus.

Short references to parts of the story are countless in English literature, but three attempts to capture the whole tragedy are outstanding. A dramatic poem entitled *The Tower beyond Tragedy,* by Robinson Jeffers, retells the story as far as the killing of Clytemnestra and Aegisthus, and probes the feelings of the characters while introducing a slight variation in the events.

The other outstanding uses of the tragedy present it in modern dress. T. S. Eliot's main character in the play *The Family Reunion* is pursued by a sense of guilt, and after causing his mother a possibly fatal shock, he begins a search for atonement. A much more direct use has been made by playwright Eugene O'Neill in *Mourning Becomes Electra,* in which the tragedy is paralleled by a nineteenth-century American family. The major difference is in Orestes' escape from the Furies: Orin Mannon can escape his tortured guilt only by suicide.

THE ROYAL HOUSE OF THEBES

The tragic story of the House of Thebes appears to have been one of the most popular subjects among Greek playwrights.

The tale is best known to us through a trilogy written by Sophocles. The story begins with *Oedipus the King*, which goes to the point of Oedipus' departure on his heartsick wanderings, after his realization of his own horrible crime.

A later play, *Oedipus at Colonus*, picks up the story. It tells how the blind king, driven from country to country, finally is permitted to find rest at Colonus, in Attica.

The story is concluded by Sophocles in *Antigone*.

Parts of the story were related by other playwrights; perhaps the most famous is Aeschylus' *Seven Against Thebes*, of which the story falls between the events of Sophocles' *Oedipus at Colonus* and *Antigone*.

OEDIPUS

ONCE long ago, a queen gave birth to a son whom she loved with all her heart. Unfortunately, her husband had been warned by an oracle that any son he had would kill him. The broken-hearted woman feared for her beloved husband and, although she was unable to restrain her tears, she allowed her child to be given to a person of the court, with orders to leave him on the mountainside until cold nights or wild beasts claimed him.

Oedipus, son of the king of Corinth, left his home to travel to the distant city of Thebes. He had received a warning from the famous oracle of Apollo at Delphi that he was doomed to kill his father, whom he loved. The young man felt he had no choice but to go so far away that he would never see his father again.

On the road to Thebes, he came to a place where three roads crossed, and there he was almost run down by a rushing chariot.

"Make way for your betters!" an old man in the carriage shouted rudely.

"I know no betters but my own parents!" Oedipus cried, enraged at the insult. He swung his stick in anger at the chariot, and swept the driver from his seat to lie wounded and bleeding in the road. The terrified horses bolted, and in the reins was entangled the startled old man who had shouted to Oedipus. He was dragged to his death there at the crossroads.

Oedipus continued on his way, but was captured by the Sphinx before reaching the city. The Sphinx was a terrible monster with a woman's face and breasts on the body of a winged lion. She was draining the very life-blood of Thebes, for, lying in wait along the roadways to and from the city, she had killed and devoured countless travellers. The Sphinx put a riddle to all whom she captured, telling them that if they answered her correctly, she would let them go. No one had yet solved her riddle.

As was her custom, she leaped upon the unsuspecting passerby, and posed her curious question.

"What creature goes upon four legs in the morning, two at noon, and three in the evening?"

Oedipus answered her without a second's hesitation:

"Man; as an infant, he crawls on all fours, as a man he walks on his two feet, and when he is old, he goes with the aid of a cane."

His answer was correct. The Sphinx, outwitted by a mortal, in mortification flung herself to her death from a high cliff, and Oedipus continued on to Thebes.

When he entered the city, he was hailed as a conqueror. The citizens rejoiced that they were free at last from the menace of the Sphinx. All honours were accorded Oedipus, and all doors were opened to him. Before long he even married the queen of the city, Jocasta, widow of dead King Laius.

Oedipus ruled as a kind and beloved king for many years. The

Thebans loved him, and his marriage to Jocasta was happy. Their union had borne four children, twin sons, Eteocles and Polyneices, and two daughters, Ismene and Antigone.

But after many years of happiness and peace, a strange blight fell upon Thebes. Crops failed, and the people grew hungry; disease spread among the Thebans, and they could not be cured. All measures to improve conditions proved useless, and in desperation Oedipus sent his trusted aide, Creon, to consult the Delphic oracle.

Creon returned with word that the gods were displeased because Thebes harboured the murderer of the former king, and the blight was a punishment upon the inhabitants. It would not be lifted until the killer had been found and driven from the city.

Oedipus, relieved to find the cause of the city's sufferings, pronounced a decree of exile upon the killer, when he should be found.

To speed matters, the king sent for a famous blind seer, Teiresias, to ask him if he could see, with his inward vision, who the king's murderer was. When the old prophet refused to answer, the king grew angry and accused Teiresias of complicity in the murder.

Stung to rage, the old man said, "You yourself are the murderer you seek."

Angered more than ever, Oedipus told the old man to get out of his sight and never come near him again. When he told his wife, Jocasta, of the words the prophet had spoken, she too was angered at the accusation.

"These prophets cause nothing but trouble," she said. "There was one, years ago, who said my husband should be killed by his own son, and I had to have my baby killed to prevent it. And then Laius was killed by robbers at a crossroads, so the whole prophecy came to nothing!"

Her words disturbed Oedipus. He asked when this had happened, and was told that it was very shortly before he had killed the Sphinx and come to the city.

At that moment a messenger arrived, bearing an urgent message to Oedipus from the queen of Corinth. His father had died.

Oedipus flung his hands to heaven and shouted his relief to the gods—the terrible prophecy that he would kill his own father had not come true!

The messenger smiled.

"You need not have feared killing the king. He was not your father," he said. "I myself took you to him, when you were a mere infant. You were given to me by an old shepherd, a servant of the king of Thebes."

Jocasta turned pale, and rushed into the palace.

As if fate were willing it, an old, ragged shepherd came to Oedipus at that very moment. He addressed the messenger as an old acquaintance.

"This is the shepherd who gave you to me," said the messenger.

And the shepherd told his story. He had been given a child by Jocasta, with orders to expose it on the mountain, but had not killed it; he had gone so far as to pierce and bind its feet, but at the last moment had given the child of Laius to a messenger, who would take the baby to be raised by the king of Corinth.

At last the whole, terrible truth had come out. All the oracles had been right: Laius had been murdered by his own son, Oedipus, whose name meant "swollen-footed" from the piercing and binding as an infant; Oedipus had really killed his own father, and, more horrible yet, had married his own mother.

A scream from within the palace bore the news to Oedipus that his wife and mother had hanged herself in horror at the grotesque deed she had unknowingly committed.

Oedipus, unable to look at the faces of men any more, tore the brooches from the robe of his dead wife and ground the pins into his eyes.

Blind and sick at soul, he left Thebes, to wander the world in exile, never able to forget his horrible sins, until at last he found peace at a lonely wood called Colonus.

IN HISTORY

The prominence of oracles and prophecies in myth reflects the tremendous influence they had in Greece. Oracles were seats of worship of a divinity, where prophecies were uttered to those who sought them.

Several distinct types are known: oracles which gave prophecies by signs, such as lots or dice; oracles of the dead, in which the souls of the departed were invoked; oracles of dreams, in which the supplicant slept in the temple and his dream was interpreted as a message; and the best-known, oral oracles.

Oral oracles were usually connected with Apollo, whose message was communicated through priests or, more commonly, priestesses, who were known as **sibyls**. They gave advice in a "state of inspiration", that is, frenzy induced by artificial means such as inhalation of steam from hot springs. The words the seer uttered were usually regarded as divine truth, though they were often ambiguous; for example, one king was told that if he marched into battle, he would destroy a great empire. He did march, and destroyed his own empire. The most renowned oral oracle was that of Apollo at Delphi.

Oracles were officially banned at the end of the fourth century A.D., when paganism was declared illegal.

ANTIGONE

FTER the exile of Oedipus, his twin sons had been elected co-rulers of Thebes. Their reigns were determined by a strange arrangement. Since they were twins, neither was assumed to be the senior; therefore, they would reign as one king, each assuming the throne in alternate years. Eteocles was to reign the first year, and Polyneices would succeed him.

However, Eteocles soon developed a taste for power, and when his year was up he was loath to retire from the throne. To carry out his evil scheme, he convinced the people that his brother Polyneices was actually cruel, deceitful, and untrustworthy, and banished Polyneices forever from the kingdom.

Polyneices raised a band of six other champions to lead an expedition against his brother. Known as the "seven against Thebes", the champions and their followers fought a valiant fight, but neither side could win a clear victory.

As a last resort and to put an end to bloodshed, the two brothers agreed to fight in single combat. They were well-matched, and the fight ended in a way which nobody had foreseen; each dealt a well-aimed blow, and by evening both brothers lay dead on the battlefield.

The throne of Thebes was then taken by Creon, the adviser of Oedipus. The old man had changed since the days when he had been the trusted and good adviser of the king. Now he was a crafty schemer, delighted at the twist of fate which had brought him the kingship. As his first proclamation, he announced that the corpse of Eteocles was to be brought from the battlefield and given a hero's burial, for he had fallen in the defence of his city. Polyneices, on the other hand, was to be considered a traitor, and his body was to be left to rot. To defy the edict meant death.

The edict of Creon was heard, but not heeded, by the sister of the dead warriors. Antigone believed, as did all the Greeks of her time, that the soul of a body left unburied would never find peace in the afterlife, but was doomed to wander restlessly for eternity. All that was necessary to save the soul of her brother Polyneices from this most terrible of all fates was to cast three handfuls of earth on the corpse. So, in spite of the orders of the king, Antigone stole out under cover of darkness to the lonely field where her brother lay. Somehow slipping past the guards, she threw on his body the precious earth which would bring his soul to rest.

When the guards brought word to Creon of the outrage, he knew immediately who was to blame. Antigone was summoned to the royal chamber.

Her answer was simple.

"I did not think, Creon," she said calmly, "that your edicts were so strong that they could outweigh the eternal laws of the gods. Their laws are immutable, and all men are required to observe them, even if this means breaking the laws of an earthly king."

Creon could find no way to convince the girl that she must admit that her deed was a crime. Reluctantly, he gave the only order which was open to him. Antigone must be put to death. She was to be immured, sealed up alive in the great wall of Thebes.

Antigone went willingly to her death, confident that she had done only what was right.

Perhaps the one to suffer most was Creon. After Antigone had been immured, the king was told that his own beloved son, Haemon, had accompanied the princess to her death and, unwilling to be separated from her, had ordered that he be sealed up in the same tomb. The final blow came when Creon's grief-stricken wife took her own life, cursing her husband's name with her dying breath.

This story comes from Euripides' tragedy, Medea.

MEDEA

OF all the treasures which Jason had brought from his voyage in search of the famed Golden Fleece, the greatest had been Medea.

Medea was a princess of Colchis, daughter of the very king from whom Jason begged the fleece. She had fallen in love with the stranger from the west at their very first meeting—in fact, the first time that she had seen him, at a distance, and heard the gentleness of his speech—and had resolved to help him.

In the course of her assistance, Medea, who was a sorceress and had divine inspiration, had committed terrible crimes. First of all, she had betrayed her country, but such a deed had seemed nothing to her, so deep was her love for the foreigner. Then she had been forced, out of love, to do worse. To save Jason's life, she had killed her own young brother, and later Jason's uncle.

The memory of these crimes faded when she and Jason settled in his land, and her longing for her own country and her own people vanished in the joy she had gained from Jason's love and the pleasure given her by their children, two beautiful sons.

But as the years went by, Jason grew tired of the wife who had done so much for him. When the opportunity arose, he decided to forsake Medea for a Corinthian princess who would bring wealth and power as a dowry.

When Medea pleaded with her husband to remember his vows, and her terrible deeds done for his sake, he laughed at her, but there was anger in his heart. She had caused him a great deal of difficulty already, he said. She had spoken roughly against the princess of Corinth when he proposed to marry, and had made the king fear for his daughter's safety. He, Jason, was going to marry the princess, come what might, and he would be glad to be rid of crime-stained Medea who, because of her unwise words, had been exiled from Jason's land.

When Jason left her, the heart of Medea was filled with grief and rage. Was she, who had betrayed all she loved for the sake of her husband, to be put aside so casually?

She knew, almost without thinking, what she was going to do.

She brought a magnificent robe, the most beautiful in her possession, and sent it as a token to the Corinthian princess. Before sending it, however, she anointed the threads with a magic liquid whose properties only she knew.

As soon as the princess put on the robe, it burst into flame, emitting heat so strong that the flesh was seared from the bone.

Medea's rival was dead, but there remained further vengeance to be taken.

Calling her sons to her side, she thought for just a moment of the fate that awaited them when her crime was discovered. Slavery, torture, and death were almost certain. In addition, Jason loved his two sons. . . .

When Jason raced to find the murderess of his princess, he arrived just in time to see Medea step into a dragon-drawn coach, which bore her away from his sight. Lying on the ground were the bloodstained corpses of his sons.

Not blaming himself for any part of the tragedy, Jason poured the curses of heaven on his witch-wife.

ECHOES IN EXPRESSION

Many words and phrases in English have a mythological origin. Imaginative interpretation of the stories in this book should make the following familiar ones clear.

Achilles' heel
apple of discord
a Cassandra
titanic
paean
Pandora's box
to pile Ossa on Pelion
Promethean
museum
Arcadian
to hector a person
beware of Greeks bearing gifts
herculean
an Augean task
to work like a Trojan
a Nessus shirt
panic
cereal
between Scylla and Charybdis
narcissistic
the Midas touch
a task of Sisyphus
sowing dragon's teeth
to drink of Lethe

an Amazon
to chase a chimaera
the thread of Ariadne
Endymion sleep
a lotus-eater
Stygian gloom
a siren
a harpy
martial
Oedipus complex
argonaut
nemesis
tantalize
vulcanize
a golden age
in the lap of the gods
Saturday
like Niobe
hydra-headed
geography
arachnid
Europe
wreath of laurels
mercurial

PRONUNCIATION KEY

Some variation may be permitted in pronouncing the Greek names. For one thing, we are not absolutely sure how the ancient Greeks pronounced some sounds; moreover, common usage has anglicized the pronunciation of some names. We have attempted to give in parentheses the most common English pronunciation which reasonably approximates the Greek.

General Rules for Pronouncing Greek Names

Greek sounds have approximately the values shown on the phonetic key:

Diphthongs

ae as in *meet*
ai as in *fine*
ei as in *face* or *meet*
oe as in *meet*
eu as in *union*

Vowels

ā as in *face*
a as in *man*
ē as in *face* (or as in *meet*)
e as in *met*
ī as in *meet* (or as in *fine*)
i as in *finish*
ō as in *over*
o as in *upon*
ū as in *union*
u as in *under*
ȳ as in *fine*
y as in *myth*

Unless indicated otherwise, the diphthongs *ae*, *ai*, *ei*, *oe* are pronounced as shown. Common usage has made the division of *eu* into two separate sounds acceptable in names of more than one syllable (e.g. *Orpheus*). Vowels which are not to be counted as diphthongs are indicated by a diaeresis (*aë*).

Similarly, common usage has made a soft *c* before *e*, *i*, and *y*, and a soft *g* before *e*, acceptable, although *c* and *g* are always correctly given only the hard pronunciation.

Ch is always pronounced as *k*.

Guide to Names Used in the Text

In the phonetic approximations, long vowels are marked—. Their pronunciation is the same as that generally accepted in the pronunciation keys that appear in dictionaries.

Accented syllables are marked ′.

170

Abydos (a' bi dos). Town on the Hellespont.

Achaeans (a kē' anz). Alternate name for early Greeks, particularly associated with Mycenae.

Acheron (a' ke ron). The river of sorrow of the underworld.

Achilles (a kil' lēs). Greek hero in the Trojan war.

Acrisius (a kri' sē us). Father of Danaë, grandfather of Perseus.

Actaeon (ak tē' on). Hunter destroyed by Artemis.

Admetus (ad mē' tus). Thessalian king served by Apollo.

Adonis (a dō' nis). Youth loved by Aphrodite.

Aegean Sea (ē gē' an). Sea bordering east of Greece.

Aegeus (ē gē' us). King of Athens, father of Theseus.

Aegisthus (ē gis' thus). Son of Thyestes, lover of Clytemnestra.

Aeneid (ē nē'id). Virgil's great epic poem.

Aeneas (ē nē' as). Trojan prince, leader of Trojans to Italy.

Aeolus (ē ō'lus). Wind god.

Aeolia (ē ō'lē a). Floating island of Aeolus in Mediterranean.

Aeschylus (ē'ski lus). Greek tragedian.

Agamemnon (a' ga mem' non). King of Mycenae, leader of Greeks against Troy.

Aiaia (ī ī' a). Circe's island, probably off western Italy.

Aeëtes (ē ā'tāz). King of Colchis, possessor of the Golden Fleece.

Ajax (ā' jaks). Name of two heroes of Trojan war.

Alcestis (al kes'tis). Wife of Admetus.

Alcinous (al ki' nō us). King of Phaeacia, father of Nausicaä.

Alcmene (alk mā' nē). Wife of Amphitryon, mother of Heracles.

Amazons (a' ma zons). Race of warrior women.

Amphion (am phē'on). Husband of Niobe.

Amphitryon (am fit' rē on). Husband of Alcmene.

Anchises (an kī'sēz). Lover of Aphrodite, father of Aeneas.

Andromache (an dro' ma kē). Wife of Hector of Troy.

Andromeda (an dro'me da). Maiden rescued by Perseus.

Antigone (an ti'go nē). Daughter of Oedipus of Thebes; buried her brother against orders.

Antinous (an ti' nō us). Overbearing suitor of Penelope.

Aphrodite (a frō dī'tē). Goddess of love (Lat. Venus).

Apollo (a pol' lō). Olympian god (sun, music, etc.).

Arachne (a rak' nē). Maiden who challenged Athene in weaving.

Arcadia (ar kā'dē a). Region of Greece, largely rural.

Ares (ā' rēz). Olympian god of war.

Arete (a rā'tē). Wife of Alcinous, mother of Nausicaä.

Argo (ar' gō). Ship built by Argus for Jason.

Argonauts (ar' gō nots). Heroes who sailed in the Argo.

Argos (ar' gos). City in Greece.

Argus (ar'gus). (1) Hundred-eyed guardian of Io.
  (2) Builder of the Argo.
  (3) Dog of Odysseus.

Ariadne (a rē ad' nā). Daughter of Minos who helped Theseus.

Artemis (ar' te mis). Goddess of the chase (Lat. Diana).

Ascanius (as kā'nē us). Son of Aeneas, also called Iulus.

Asclepius (as klē' pē us). Son of Apollo; god of medicine.

Astyanax (a stȳ'an aks). Son of Hector and Andromache.

Asphodel Fields (as' fō del). Underworld region.

Atalanta (a ta lan' ta). Huntress of Calydon.

Athene (a thē' nē; commonly a thē'na). Goddess of wisdom, war, etc. (Lat. Minerva).

Athens (a'thenz). Major city of Greece.

Atlas (at' las). Titan, leader in war, bearer of the sky.

Atreus (a' trē us). King of Mycenae, father of Agamemnon and Menelaus.

Augeias (o gē' as). King of Elis whose stables Heracles cleaned.

171

Aulis (ō'lis). Greek port where Iphigeneia was sacrificed.

Bacchanalia (ba ka nā'lē a). Wild orgy.
Bacchus (ba'kus). *See* Dionysus.
Bellerophon (be lair'o fon). Killer of Chimaera.
Blest, Isles of the. Afterlife home of the greatest heroes.
Briseis (bri sā'is). Captive of Achilles.

Callisto (ka lis' tō). Follower of Artemis, changed into a bear.
Calliope (ka lī'ō pē). Muse of epic poetry.
Calypso (ka lip'sō). Sorceress who looked after Odysseus.
Carthage (kar'thage). City of northern Africa.
Cassandra (ka san'dra). Trojan princess whose prophecies were never believed.
Castor (kas'tor). Son of Zeus and Leda, twin of Polydeuces.
Caucasus (ko'ka sus). Mountains east of Black Sea, where Prometheus was bound.
Centaur (commonly sen' tor). Half-horse, half-human creature.
Cerberus (commonly ser'ber us). Three-headed watchdog of Hades.
Ceryneian hind (commonly se ri' nē an). Deer captured by Heracles.
Chaos (kā'os). Formless void that existed before creation.
Charon (kā'ron). Ferryman across river Styx.
Charybdis (ka rib'dis). Monster, probably in Straits of Messina.
Cheiron (kī' ron). Centaur, teacher of several famous heroes.
Chimaera (ki mē'ra). Lion-goat-snake monster, killed by Bellerophon.
Chryseis (krī'sē is). Trojan girl, captive of Agamemnon.
Chrysothemis (kri so' the mis). Daughter of Agamemnon and Clytemnestra.
Ciconians (commonly si sō'nē anz). People encountered by Odysseus.
Cimmerians, Land of (commonly sim mair' ē anz). Land at the edge of the world.
Circe (commonly ser'sē). Enchantress visited by Odysseus.
Clio (klē'ō). Muse of history.
Clymene (kli me'nē). Mother of Phaëthon.

Clytemnestra (klī tem nes'tra). Wife of Agamemnon.
Clytie (klī'tē). Girl who loved Appollo.
Cnossos (k nos' sus). Capital of Crete.
Cocytus (ko ky'tus). River of lamentation of the underworld.
Colchis (kol'kis). Country bordering on Black Sea.
Corinth (ko'rinth). A major city of Greece.
Creon (krē'on). Adviser to Oedipus, later king of Thebes.
Crete (krēt). Large island in Mediterranean Sea.
Creusa (krā ū' sa). Wife of Aeneas, lost in Troy.
Cronus (krō'nus). Titan king, son of Uranus and Gaea (Lat. Saturn).
Cupid (kū'pid). *See* Eros.
Cyclops (commonly sī'klops). Race of one-eyed giants.
Cynthia. (sin' thē a). *See* Artemis.
Cyparissus (commonly sī pa ris' sus). Boy turned by Apollo into tree of mourning.
Cyprus (commonly sī'prus). Large Mediterranean island.
Cythera (commonly si'thē ra). Mediterranean island.

Daedalus (dē'da lus). Builder of labyrinth, father of Icarus.
Danaë (da'na ē). Mother of Perseus.
Daphne (daf'nē). Maiden pursued by Apollo.
Deianeira (dā an ā'ra). Wife of Heracles.
Delphi (del'fē). Town and region in Greece.
Demeter (dē mē'ter). Goddess of the fields (Lat. Ceres).
Deucalion (dū kā'lē on). Son of Prometheus, survivor of Flood.
Diana (dī a' na). *See* Artemis.
Dido (dī'dō). Queen of Carthage visited by Aeneas.
Diomedes (dī o mē'dēz). King killed by Heracles.
Dionysus (dī o nī'sus). God of wine (Lat. Bacchus).

Earth. *See* Gaea.
Echo (e'kō). Nymph who loved Narcissus.
Electra (e lek'tra). Daughter of Agamemnon and Clytemnestra.

Eleusis (e lū' sis). Seat of worship of Demeter and Persephone.

Elysium (e lis'ē um). Underworld abode of happiness.

Endymion (en di'mē on). Sleeping youth loved by Artemis.

Epaphus (e pa' fus). Son of Zeus who taunted Phaëthon.

Epimetheus (commonly e pi mē'thē us). Titan, brother of Prometheus, husband of Pandora.

Erato (e rat' o). Muse of love poetry.

Erebus (e're bus). Part of the underworld (originally Darkness).

Eremanthyan boar (e ri man'thē an). Boar captured by Heracles.

Erinnyes (e rin'ū āz). Vengeance deities, later changed to Eumenides.

Eris (e'ris). Goddess of strife, sister of Ares.

Eros (e'ros). God of love (Lat. Cupid).

Eteocles (e tā'o klēz). Son of Oedipus of Thebes.

Eumenides (ū men'i dēz). See Erinnyes.

Euripides (ū rip' i dēz). Greek playwright.

Europa (ū rō'pa). Maiden abducted by Zeus.

Eurydice (ū ri' di sē). Wife of Orpheus.

Eurylochus (ū ri' lo kus). Companion of Odysseus.

Eurymachus (ū ri' ma kus). Suitor of Penelope.

Eurystheus (ū ris'thūs). King who imposed Heracles' labours.

Euterpe (ū ter' pē). Muse of lyric poetry.

Fates. (Gk. Moirai; Lat. Parcae). Goddesses who determined human destiny; named Clotho, Lachesis, Atropos.

Furies. See Erinnyes.

Gaea (gē'a). Goddess of Earth, wife of Uranus (Lat. Tellus).

Galatea (ga la tē' a). Woman created from statue carved by Pygmalion.

Ganymede (ga' nē mēd). Cupbearer favoured by Zeus.

Geryon (ge'ry on). Three-torsoed king fought by Heracles.

Gordius (gor'dē us). Phrygian king associated with Midas.

Gorgons (gor'gonz). Female monsters.

Graces (Gk, Charites; Lat. Gratiae). Goddesses of gentleness.

Graiae (grī' ē). Gray-haired women, protectresses of the Gorgons.

Hades (hā'dēz). God of the underworld. (Lat. Dis, Pluto).

Haemon (hē'mon). Son of Creon, lover of Antigone.

Harpies (har'pēz). Bird-women who snatched food, bodies.

Hebe (hē'bē). Cupbearer of the gods.

Hecabe (he'ka bē). Wife of Priam.

Hecate (he'ka tē). Goddess associated with witchcraft.

Hecatoncheires (he'ka ton kā'rāz). Hundred-handed sons of Gaea.

Hector (hek'tor). Trojan hero.

Hecuba (he'kū ba). Latin form of name of Priam's wife. See Hecabe.

Helen (he'len). Wife of Menelaus, abducted by Paris.

Hellespont (hel'le spont). Strait, now Dardanelles.

Hephaestus (he fē'stus). Smith-god (Lat. Vulcan).

Hera (he'ra). Wife of Zeus, queen of gods (Lat. Juno).

Heracles (he'ra klēz). Greatest Greek hero (Lat. Hercules).

Hercules. See Heracles.

Hero (he' rō). Maiden loved by Leander.

Hermes (her'mēz). Messenger-god (Lat. Mercury).

Hesiod (he' si od). Early poet, author of *Theogony*.

Hesperides (hes pair'i dēz). Daughters of Night, guardians of Hera's golden apple tree.

Hestia (hes'tē a). Hearth-goddess (Lat. Vesta).

Hippolyta (hip po'li ta). Amazon queen.

Hippolytus (hip po'li tus). Son of Theseus and Hippolyta, beloved by Phaedra.

Homer (hō'mer). Author of the *Iliad* and the *Odyssey*.

Hundred-Handed Ones (Gr. Hecatoncheires). Three sons of Uranus and Gaea.

Hyacinthus (commonly hī a sin'thus). Friend of Apollo, accidentally killed by the god.

Hydra (hī'dra). Many-headed snake monster.

Hylas (hī'las). Friend of Heracles, lost on Argo voyage.

Hyperboreans (hī per bo' rē anz). Nymphs of the North.

Hyperion (hī pē'rē on). Titan.

Icarus (i' ka rus). Son of Daedalus, fell into sea.

Iliad (i' lē ad). Epic poem of the Trojan war.

Ilium (i' lē um). Alternate name for Troy.

Io (ī'ō or ē'ō). Girl loved by Zeus, turned to heifer.

Ino (ī'nō). Sea goddess.

Iphicles (i' fi klēz). Half-brother of Heracles.

Iphigeneia (i' fi ge ni'a). Daughter of Agamemnon, sacrificed at Aulis.

Iris (ī'ris). Rainbow goddess.

Ismaros (is ma' ros). Land of the Ciconians.

Ismene (is mā'nē). Daughter of Oedipus, sister of Antigone.

Ithaca (i' tha ka). Rocky home of Odysseus.

Iulus (ī ū'lus). Alternate name for Ascanius, son of Aeneas.

Jason (jā'son). Hero of expedition for Golden Fleece.

Jocasta (jō kas'ta). Queen of Thebes, mother and wife of Oedipus.

Jove. (jōv). See Zeus.

Juno. (jū'nō). See Hera.

Jupiter. (jū'pi ter). See Zeus.

Laertes (lā er'tāz). King of Ithaca, father of Odysseus.

Laestrygonians (lē stri go' nē anz). Land of. Visited by Odysseus.

Laius (lā' us). King of Thebes, husband of Jocasta.

Laocoön (lā o' kō on). Trojan priest crushed by serpents.

Latinus (la tī'nus). King of Latium who received Aeneas.

Latium (la'tē um). Region of Italy around site of Rome.

Latona. (la tō' na). See Leto.

Lavinia (la vi'nē a). Daughter of Latinus, married Aeneas.

Leander (lē an' der). Lover of Hero.

Leda (lē'da). Woman loved by Zeus, mother of Helen, Clytemnestra, Castor, and Polydeuces.

Lesbos (les'bos). Aegean island noted for early poets.

Lethe (lē'thē). Forgetfulness river in the underworld.

Leto (lē'tō). Titaness, mother of Apollo and Artemis (Lat. Latona).

Libya (li'bē a). African country.

Lotus-Eaters. North Africans visited by Odysseus.

Lydia (li'dē a). Country in Asia Minor.

Maenads (mē'nads). Wild female followers of Dionysus.

Maia (mī'a). Mother of Hermes.

Malea, Cape (ma' lē a). Point of Greece passed by Odysseus.

Mars. (marz). See Ares.

Medea (me dē'a). Princess of Colchis, helper and wife of Jason.

Medusa (me dū'sa). Mortal Gorgon slain by Perseus.

Melpomene (mel po' me nē). Muse of tragedy.

Menelaus (me ne lā'us). Brother of Agamemnon, husband of Helen.

Mercury. (mer' kūr ē). See Hermes.

Metis (mē'tis). Titaness swallowed by Zeus.

Midas (mī'das). Phrygian king afflicted with golden touch.

Minerva. (mi ner' va). See Athene.

Minoan civilization (mi nō'an). Name given to ancient Cretan civilization.

Minos (mī'nos). King of Crete.

Minotaur (mī'no tor). Half-bull, half-human Cretan monster kept in labyrinth.

Moirai. (moi' rē). See Fates.

Mnemosyne (m'ne mo'si nē). Mother of Muses.

Muses (mū'sez). Daughters of Zeus, in charge of poetry, arts, etc.

Mycenae (commonly mī sē'nē). Major city of ancient Greece.

Narcissus (commonly nar sis'sus). Youth who loved his reflection.

Nausicaä (no si'ka a). Phaeacian princess who received Odysseus.

Nemea (ne' mē a). Valley where lived invulnerable lion.

Nemesis (ne'me sis). Goddess of retribution.

Neoptolemus (nē op to'le mus). Son of Achilles, killer of Priam.

Neptune. (nep' tūn). See Poseidon.

Nereus (nē'rūs). Sea-god.

Nessus (ne'sus). Centaur who pursued Deianeira.

Nestor (nes'tor). King of Pylus, wisest of Greek heroes in Trojan war.

Niobe (nī ō'bē or nī'ō be). Daughter of Tantalus, turned into weeping rock.

Oceanus (o kē an'us). Titan; stream encircling the earth.

Odysseus (o di'sūs). Greek hero from Ithaca who made ten-year voyage returning from Troy (Lat. Ulysses, Ulixes).

Odyssey (o'di sē). Epic poem, voyage of Odysseus.

Oedipus (ē'di pus). King of Thebes, unknowingly killed father and married mother.

Oenone (ē nō'nē). Nymph loved by Paris.

Ogygia (o gi'gē a). Calypso's island, off Italy.

Olympus, Mount (ō lim'pus). Home of the gods, in Thessaly.

Orestes (o res'tāz). Son of Agamemnon and Clytemnestra, avenger of his father's murder.

Orpheus (commonly or'fē us). Thracian musician.

Orthrus (or' thrus). Two-headed hound-monster.

Ossa, Mount (os' sa). Mountain used in war with Titans.

Ovid (o'vid). Latin poet, author of *Metamorphoses*.

Pactolus (pak to' lus). River in which Midas bathed.

Pallas (pal'las). (1) Friend of Athene, accidentally killed.
(2) Title adopted by Athene.

Pan (pan). Shepherd god.

Pandora (pan dō'ra). Wife of Epimetheus; opened jar of evils.

Parcae. (par' kī). See Fates.

Paris (pa' ris). Trojan prince, abductor of Helen. Also called Alexander.

Parnassus (par nas'sus). Phocian mountain, home of the Muses.

Parthenon (par'the non). Athenian temple dedicated to Athene (the "maiden's chamber").

Patroclus (pa tro'klus). Friend of Achilles, killed by Hector.

Pegasus (pe'ga sus). Winged horse captured by Bellerophon.

Peleus (pē'lūs). Father of Achilles.

Pelias (pe'lē as). Usurping uncle of Jason.

Pelion, Mount (pē'lē on). Mountain in Thessaly, used in war with Titans.

Peloponnese (pe' lo pon nes'). Southern part of Greece.

Pelops (pe'lops). Son of Tantalus, served by his father to the gods.

Penelope (pe ne'lō pē). Faithful wife of Odysseus.

Persephone (per se'fō nē). Daughter of Demeter, wife of Hades.

Perseus (per'sūs). Hero who killed Medusa.

Phaeacia (fē ā'sha). Land visited by Odysseus.

Phaedra (fē'dra, commonly fe'dra). Wife of Theseus, who loved Hippolytus.

Phaëthon (fā'e thon). Son of Apollo, who tried to drive chariot of the sun.

Phidias (fī'dē as). Sculptor associated with Parthenon.

Phlegethon (fle'ge thon). Fiery river of the underworld.

Phoebus (fē'bus). A name of Apollo.

Phrygia (fri'gē a). Region in Asia Minor.

Pindar (pin'dar). Greek poet, composer of odes.

Pluto (plū' tō). See Hades.

Pollux (pol' luks). See Polydeuces.

Polydeuces (po lē dū'sēz). Son of Zeus and Leda, twin of Castor.

Polyhymnia (po lē him'nē a). Muse of hymns.

Polyneices (po lē nī'sēz). Son of Oedipus, brother of Eteocles.

Polyphemus (po lē fē'mus). Cyclops encountered by Odysseus.

Poseidon (po sī'don). God of the sea (Lat. Neptune).

Priam (prī'am). King of Troy.

Prometheus (commonly prō mē'thē us). Titan who helped mankind.

Prosperpina. (pro' ser pē' na). *See* Persephone.

Psyche (sī'kē). Bride of Eros.

Pygmalion (pig mā'lē on). Sculptor who fell in love with his creation.

Pyrrha (pē'ra). Wife of Deucalion, daughter of Epimetheus.

Pythia (pi'thē a). Apollo's oracle at Delphi.

Python (pī'thon). Serpent killed by Apollo.

Rhea (rē'a). Wife of Cronus, mother of Zeus (Lat. Ops).

Samos (sa'mos). Aegean island, birthplace of Hera.

Saturn. (sat' urn). *See* Cronus.

Satyr (sā'ter). Goat-man (Lat. faun).

Scylla (sil'la). Six-headed monster living opposite Charybdis.

Semele (se' me lē). Mother of Dionysus, consumed by Zeus' glory.

Sestos (ses'tos). Town on the Hellespont.

Sibyl (si'bil). Prophetess living at Cumae in Italy.

Silenus (sī lē'nus). Tutor of Dionysus.

Sinon (si'non). Greek who tricked Trojans into accepting wooden horse.

Siren (sī'ren). Sweet singers who tried to lure Odysseus.

Sisyphus (si'si fus). Sufferer in the underworld.

Sophocles (so'fo klēz). Greek tragedian (*Oedipus the King*).

Sparta (spar' ta). Major city and region of Greece.

Sphinx (sfinks). Female monster who molested Thebes, destroyed by Oedipus.

Stymphalian birds (stim fā'lē an). Bronze-beaked birds killed by Heracles.

Styx (stiks). "Abhorrent" river of the underworld.

Syrinx (sy'rinks). Maiden pursued by Pan, changed into reeds.

Talus (tā'lus). (1) Bronze giant on Crete. (2) Nephew and apprentice of Daedalus.

Tantalus (tan'ta lus). Man who offended gods.

Tartarus (tar'tar us). Place of torment in the underworld; sometimes used for the whole underworld.

Tauris (to'ris). Modern Crimea; land where Iphigeneia was taken.

Teiresias (tā rē'sē as). Blind seer of Thebes.

Telemachus (te le'ma kus). Son of Odysseus.

Tenedos (te'ne dos). Island near Troy.

Terpsichore (terp si ko'rē). Muse of dancing.

Thalia (thā'lē a). Muse of comedy.

Thebes (thēbz). A major city of ancient Greece.

Themis (the'mis). Titaness, representative of law, order, and hospitality.

Theseus (thē'sūs). Athenian prince who killed the Minotaur.

Thessaly (the'sa lē). Area of northern Greece.

Thetis (the'tis). Sea-nymph, wife of Peleus, mother of Achilles.

Thrace (thrās). Region north of the Aegean Sea.

Thyestes (thī es'tēz). Brother of Atreus.

Tiber (tī'ber). River on whose banks Rome was built.

Titans (tī'tanz). Children of Uranus and Gaea.

Triton (trī'ton). Sea-god, son of Poseidon.

Troy. City in Asia Minor (Lat. sometimes Ilium).

Turnus (tur'nus). Italian king who opposed Aeneas' marriage.

Tyndareus (tin da' rūs). King of Sparta, husband of Leda.

Urania (ū rā'nē a). Muse of astronomy.

Uranus (ū rā'nus). Husband of Gaea, mutilated by Cronus.

Venus. (ve' nus). *See* Aphrodite.

Virgil (vir'gil). Latin poet, author of the *Aeneid*.

Vulcan. (vul'can). *See* Hephaestus.

Zeus (zūs). Son of Cronus and Rhea, king of the Olympian gods.

INDEX

7 8 9 10   124775   88 87 86 85